THE METHODS OF CONTEMPORARY THOUGHT

J. M. BOCHEŃSKI
University of Fribourg, Switzerland

THE METHODS OF

CONTEMPORARY THOUGHT

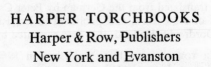

HARPER TORCHBOOKS
Harper & Row, Publishers
New York and Evanston

THE METHODS OF CONTEMPORARY THOUGHT

Printed in the United States of America.

This book was originally published under the title DIE ZEITGE-
NÖSSISCHEN DENKMETHODEN by Francke Verlag, Bern, Switzer-
land. It was translated from the German by Peter Caws, Carnegie
Corporation of New York, and published in English in 1965 by
D. Reidel, Dordrecht, Holland. It is here reprinted by permission.

First HARPER TORCHBOOK edition published in 1968 by Harper
& Row, Publishers, Incorporated,
49 East 33rd Street, New York, N.Y. 10016.

TABLE OF CONTENTS

PROLOGUE

CHAPTER I

INTRODUCTION

CHAPTER II

THE PHENOMENOLOGICAL METHOD

CHAPTER III

SEMIOTIC METHODS

CHAPTER IV

THE AXIOMATIC METHOD

CHAPTER V

REDUCTIVE METHODS

EPILOGUE

TRANSLATOR'S INTRODUCTION

Professor Bocheński, as he himself points out in the prologue, is a logician; he is best known in England and the United States for his work in the history of logic, and more recently in Soviet and East European philosophy. But he has taught philosophy for many years – in Rome, in Switzerland, and on a number of visits to the United States – and in this book provides an elementary introduction to contemporary work in the field. As a means to this end he has chosen to deal with four alternative *methods* employed by philosophers in the twentieth century.

Philosophical methodology has not attracted much attention, in English-speaking circles, as a distinct branch of the discipline of philosophy; the term "methodologist", if used at all, would ordinarily be taken to refer to somebody concerned with scientific rather than philosophical method. When, therefore, Professor Bocheński refers, as he frequently does, to "contemporary methodologists", meaning people who debate the respective merits of phenomenology and mathematical logic as ways of approaching the world, the phrase has an odd ring. But philosophical methodology really makes a great deal more sense than scientific methodology. In science methodology is almost superfluous; given all the available information and a reasonably clear idea of what is wanted, there is usually not much ambiguity as to the means of getting it, or not much that could be resolved by mere argument. In philosophy, on the other hand, it is much less clear what is wanted, or what counts as information, and the method employed may have a decisive influence on the formulation of the problem itself, as well as on the nature of any possible solution to it. When a situation like this arises in science (as happened, for example, in the development of the theory of relativity and quantum theory) it is recognized at once that the principles involved are, at bottom, philosophical.

In addition to the comparative novelty of this approach one further feature of the book is worth remark. Philosophy in the twentieth century, to oversimplify matters somewhat, has been split between two traditions, the continental and the British (although a good deal of recent work in the latter has been done in Warsaw, Vienna, and the United States). The first is rationalist and metaphysical, the second empiricist and logical; and there has been regrettably little exchange of ideas between them. But in this book both are represented; and it turns out that their methods have more in common, from the point of view of analytical rigour, than their proponents, preoccupied with certain obvious strengths and weaknesses – the relevance but the apparent unreliability of metaphysics, the reliability but the apparent irrelevance of logical analysis – are always ready to admit. And one of Professor Bocheński's objectives, as he indicates in the epilogue, has been to draw attention to this fact as a possible basis for a much-needed unification of philosophy.

In the preparation of this translation I have had access to a rough draft in English by Stanley Godman. This has been of the greatest possible use; indeed, although the responsibility for the final version, with all its defects, is entirely mine, Mr. Godman deserves credit for a good share of the work. For valuable assistance with some German passages I am grateful also to Brigitta Schreck. I have kept at hand the Spanish translation by Raimundo Drudis Baldrich, through which I first became acquainted with the book, and by comparison with which this translation has been improved at several points. It has been further improved, as to accuracy, by Professor Bocheński's own comments, and as to style by my wife's most helpful criticism. Finally I am indebted to a number of typists, but especially to my secretary, Mrs. Joan Wicks, for help in the preparation of the manuscript.

PETER CAWS

New York, February 1965

PROLOGUE

This short book attempts to give an account of the most important contemporary methods of thought which are of general interest (i.e. used in many fields), in a very elementary way and in accordance with the views of present-day methodologists.

In order to prevent misunderstandings, it may be useful to explain rather more closely the limitations of our enquiry.

1. We are concerned with *methods* of thought; the book belongs to the province of general methodology, that is the department of logic which deals with the application of the laws of logic to the practice of thought. It should be noted that the book has been written by a logician; this has probably resulted in some one-sidedness in the emphasis on the logical in the methods described. (On the other hand, logical elements seem to be all-important in methodology.)

2. The contents of the book are all very elementary. Quite important theories such as, for example, the theory of probability or the details of the historical method have either been completely disregarded or only touched on. This was necessary in order to be able to concentrate the essentials into a few pages. In particular everything has been excluded that would presuppose any knowledge of mathematics – except for quite simple calculations – and of mathematical logic. Technical terminology has also been partly excluded in order to make it easier for the non-professional to understand the text.

3. In spite of its dogmatic manner, the book is simply expository. The author accepts no responsibility for the rules and arguments which he describes. If he were to write a systematic methodology it might turn out to be a book quite different from this one.

4. The views expounded are those of methodologists, not those of scientists themselves. To that extent, therefore, it is a book about contemporary philosophy. But the word "philosophy" must be understood here in a very narrow and unfamiliar sense, since genuinely philosophical questions, for example, those concerning the nature of logic or the basis of induction, have been almost entirely ignored. The book is concerned with the methods themselves, not with their interpretation and ultimate justification.

1

CHAPTER I

INTRODUCTION

1. TERMINOLOGY

In order to give a clear account of contemporary methodological theories we require a terminology with precisely established meanings. For this reason it will be necessary to preface the discussion proper with some terminological definitions. The purpose of this is not to establish any theoretical principles but to obtain rules for using certain words and phrases; these rules will often take the form of propositions which could also be used to make assertions about things: but here all that matters is the way in which the terms in question will be used in this book.

On the whole, our terminology forms part of the common usage of philosophers; certain expressions, however, are used in different ways by different thinkers. In such cases it has been necessary to choose a single meaning, and in this sense what we are about to say is conventional: that such and such an expression is to be used in such and such a way.

Ontological Terminology

The world is made up of *things* (elements, substances), such as mountains, plants, men, etc., which are characterized by various *properties* – e.g. colours, shapes, dispositions, etc. – and linked one with another by a variety of relations. The general philosophical name for everything which is or can be is "being" *(Seiendes);* even such things as properties and relationships will thus be called "beings". It is possible to distinguish two aspects in every being: *what* it is – its nature, its "whatness", its essence – and the aspect which consists in the fact *that* the being is – its *Dasein,* its existence.

If a being is modified in some way – e.g. if a thing is red, or a geo-metrical figure has twice the area of another – we are confronted with a state of affairs. States of affairs are not independent of one another. On the contrary, it often happens that *if* one state of affairs is the case, *then* another is also the case. The world may be thought of as an inter-related pattern of states of affairs. Indeed it is itself a colossal and extremely complicated state of affairs, in which everything that is or can be is connected with everything else in an endless network of relation-ships. Of course this is not to say that it would not be possible to use more or fewer categories. In fact it has been asserted in the history of philosophy that, for example, there are no things but only properties or relations; other thinkers have taught that there is only one thing. There are also some thinkers who, on the contrary, trace everything back not to a *one* but to a *many*. The list of such theories could easily be extended.

From the methodological standpoint, however, these discussions are of slight importance. Perhaps a deeper analysis would permit us to accept one of these fundamental points of view. But in the practical business of knowledge all the categories mentioned are constantly used. And it is a striking fact that we find far-reaching agreement with respect to these categories among the leading thinkers of Western culture: Plato, Aristotle, Plotinus, St. Augustine, St. Thomas, Spinoza, Leibniz, Kant, Hegel, Husserl, Whitehead all use a language in which the names of our categories occur, whatever may be their understanding of the world in itself.

Psychological Terminology

Methodology is concerned with knowledge. What knowledge is, how-ever, is a difficult and much disputed question. The sense which is to be given to this term must now therefore be specified.

(1) Knowledge is taken to be something *mental,* something which is to be found in the mind and only there: knowledge is here limited to *human* knowledge. Further it is considered not in the sense of an act or a process, but rather of a *condition*, or more precisely a *state*. Knowledge is that in virtue of which a man can be called a "knower" – just as bravery is that in virtue of which he is called "brave", and strength that in virtue of which we say of a bull or a motor that it is "strong". From this it follows that there is no such thing as knowledge "in itself" or knowledge apart from the mind of some human being; all knowledge is the knowledge of individual men.

There is admittedly much talk in present-day philosophy about supra-individual knowledge. But this usage comes about either because the *object* of knowledge is thought of, or because of the metaphysical pre-supposition of a collective subject, such as the Hegelian objective spirit. For methodological purposes it is convenient to make a distinction between knowledge as mental phenomenon and the content of that knowledge, and the metaphysical (and incidentally very questionable) thesis referred to is therefore quite insignificant, since ultimately method can be applied only by an individual, and not by such an allegedly objective spirit.

(2) Knowledge always has an object: that which is known. And this object is always a state of affairs. A thing or a property or a relation cannot be known, strictly speaking: if anything is known, it is always that the thing or property or relation in question occurs in a certain way in a state of affairs.

(3) The object is, as it were, *pictured* in knowledge. Things, properties and relations are represented in this way by means of *concepts*, states of affairs by means of *propositions*. It follows from what has just been said that a concept is not sufficient for knowledge: knowledge refers to states of affairs, and these are represented first of all by means of propositions. Propositions, then, are the first requirement for knowledge.

(4) The representations referred to can be considered either subjectively or objectively. Subjectively considered, they are to be taken as mental *patterns*, which constitute a part of the human mind; seen objectively it is a question of their *content*, what is represented by these patterns. This content might be thought to be something real, a being, namely the being which is known. But this is not the case. To show this it is enough to point out that there are also false propositions – and such propositions obviously have a content, they are not merely mental patterns, and yet they are not representations of the real world.

The expressions "concept" and "proposition" are thus ambiguous: a distinction must be made between the *subjective concept* and the *subjective proposition* – which are mental patterns – and the *objective concept* and the *objective proposition* – which are not mental patterns but the contents of the corresponding subjective concepts or propositions.

(5) All cognition comes about through a mental process; the result of this process is knowledge. This process is not a state but an *activity* of the subject. Here it will be called *the acquisition of knowledge (Erkennen)*.

4

The acquisition of knowledge, like knowledge itself, is something mental, something attaching to the individual person. As opposed to objective concepts and propositions, however, there is no such thing as "the objective acquisition of knowledge"; this would be an absurdity.

The acquisition of knowledge in the full sense culminates in a *judgement*, by which an objective proposition is asserted (or denied). The corresponding "lower" process of cognition, which leads to the formation of the subjective concept and to the conceiving of the objective concept, will be called "concept formation".

In fact both acts are closely connected in the process of cognition; both have a very complicated structure which will not be discussed further here. It may be noted that some thinkers (such as the scholastics and Kant) use the word "judgement" in the sense given to the word "proposition" in this book. But in our terminology a judgement is always a process, whereas a proposition is an objective pattern.

(6) It is necessary to distinguish between the acquisition of knowledge and *thinking*. The expression "thinking" will be given a wider connotation: it is to be taken as meaning a mental or intellectual movement from one object to another. Such a movement need not necessarily be an acquisition of knowledge. It is possible, for example, to think in such a way as to remember different things one after another in a moment of leisure. The acquisition of knowledge would then be conceived as *serious thinking*, as the kind of thinking which is intent on knowledge.

Semiotic Terminology

In order to communicate our concepts and propositions to others, and to make our own thinking easier, we use *signs*, above all a written or oral *language*, consisting of words or similar symbols. The two following facts are important in this connection:

(1) Language does not represent things directly, but rather objective concepts and objective propositions. We do not say how things are, but rather how we think of them. This is a very important observation, the failure to take account of which may lead to serious errors.

(2) Language does not always represent objective concepts and propositions adequately. It frequently happens that a linguistic sign represents several objective forms (ambiguity) or that several signs represent the same form (synonymy).

5

There is a natural and perfectly justified tendency to develop language so that it shall represent objective concepts and propositions as adequately as possible. But this remains an ideal that is seldom achieved. Since language plays an overwhelmingly important part in the acquisition of human knowledge (if only for the reason that this knowledge is socially conditioned, that is, becomes known through what has been discovered by other men, and by means of language), linguistic analysis, the interpretation of language, is one of the most important items in the method of cognition.

A sign for an objective concept will be called a "name" and a sign for an objective proposition a "statement". This leads to the following table, which summarizes our terminology:

Domain of the real:	being	state of affairs
Processes of cognition:	concept formation	judgement
Objective forms:	objective concept	objective proposition
Subjective forms:	subjective concept	subjective proposition
Language:	name	statement

This is, needless to say, merely a provisional guide which will be amplified below.

Terminology of the Theory of Knowledge

An objective proposition – and therefore also a subjective proposition and a meaningful statement – is always either *true* or *false*. The meaning of these expressions is defined provisionally as follows: a proposition is true just when it comes true, that is, when the corresponding state of affairs is the case. It is false just when it does not come true, that is, when the corresponding state of affairs is not the case. The term "truth" will therefore be taken to mean "the property of a proposition or statement which consists in the fact that the corresponding state of affairs is the case". The meaning of the term "falsity" can be defined analogously.

This is, needless to say, only one of the very numerous meanings of the term "truth", since it has not only, for example, in the language of the art critics, at least a dozen different meanings, but even in logic itself it is used in several senses. In addition many philosophers give the term different, more or less legitimate (i.e. expedient) meanings.

The meaning given has been chosen, however, firstly because this one occurs in every science even though it may be accompanied by others, and secondly because it seems that all other definitions presuppose it in some way. If it is said, for example, that a proposition is true when it speaks to the human condition of the person who receives it, then on a higher level the question is: is it *true* that this proposition speaks to the human condition etc.? And here "true" can obviously only have the above meaning. If someone were to maintain that every truth is relative (that is, were to ascribe to the term a quite different meaning from ours) then one would have to ask in *our* sense: is that true?

However that may be, this much seems certain, that every science strives to establish true statements (in the above sense): that is the ultimate aim of the acquisition of scientific knowledge. This is naturally not to say that such a goal is always attained, nor that it is even attainable in every domain; but the tendency towards this goal clearly determines every acquisition of knowledge and therefore the meaning of "truth" adopted here is fundamental for methodology.

This goal can be reached in two different ways: (1) by inspecting the state of affairs (literally or mentally): if one wishes to know, for example, whether the proposition "This table is brown" is true, it is enough to look at the table; this will be called the *direct* acquisition of knowledge; (2) by inspecting, not the state of affairs in question, but other states of affairs, and drawing conclusions from them about the first. This will be called the *indirect* acquisition of knowledge. It should be noted that every interpretation of signs is a form of indirect acquisition of knowledge: on the one hand we see material signs (such as small ink marks), on the other hand we see (mentally) certain general connections between such signs and states of affairs. From this we draw conclusions as to the meaning of the signs in the particular concrete case.

Admittedly the phenomenon of the indirect acquisition of knowledge is very curious – it is not easy at first to see how knowledge can possibly be acquired in this way. But it is beyond all question that we do come to know many things indirectly, and that there appears to be an admixture of the indirect in every acquisition of knowledge. The nature of the indirect acquisition of knowledge is also very problematical. Here, however, we are concerned exclusively with methodology, so that we shall not consider these problems further, but merely presuppose the fact that such a process does take place.

2. Logic, methodology and science

For an understanding of methodological theories a short account of the place of methodology in the system of the sciences is necessary. For this purpose we must deal briefly with the concepts of logic – of which methodology is a part – and of science.

Logic

There are few terms even in the technical language of philosophy which are as ambiguous as the term "logic". Disregarding all the meanings which have nothing to do with inference, there still remains an ambiguity, or, more precisely, a tripartite division of the domain covered by this term. Logic, as the science of inference, comprises three disciplines which should be kept sharply distinct.

(1) *Formal Logic*. Formal logic deals with the so-called laws of logic, i.e. propositions according to which one must make inferences if one wishes to proceed from true propositions to true propositions. The nature of formal logic again poses difficult problems, but it is easy to show by a few examples what it is concerned with. Such an example is the well-known *modus ponendo ponens:* "If *A*, then *B*; *A*, therefore *B*." This is a law of logic. Whatever statements are substituted for the letters "*A*" and "*B*", the whole statement will be true – in other words from a true statement we can derive, by means of this law, another true statement. Another example is the syllogism (in the mood *Barbara*): "If all *M* are *P* and all *S* are *M*, then all *S* are *P*." Formal logic is concerned with such logical laws, their formulation and organization, the methods of their verification, etc.

(2) *Methodology*. One might think that formal logic would suffice for the analysis of the indirect acquisition of knowledge. And yet this is not the case. In the course of scientific research it becomes clear that the same laws of logic can be applied in different ways. A law of logic is one thing, an inference drawn in accordance with such a law quite

another. Thus, for example, the well-known division of methods of thought into deductive and inductive consists fundamentally not in the use of different laws of logic but in a different use of the same laws. Methodology is precisely the theory of the application of the laws of logic to various fields.

(3) *Philosophy of Logic.* Finally it is possible to ask various questions about logic itself and the nature of its laws. What is it all about? Linguistic forms, mental processes, objective structures or even states of affairs? What exactly is a law of logic? How do we know that it is true? And is it possible to speak of truth in this connection at all? Are the laws of logic valid "in themselves" or are they merely assumptions? – Furthermore, the laws of logic often contain the expression "for all". What does this really mean? Is there anything altogether general? If there is, where is it to be found? In the mental, in the objective, in the real – or perhaps only in the linguistic realm? Such and similar questions obviously belong neither to formal logic nor to methodology: they form the subject-matter of the philosophy of logic.

The most important thing is to maintain a strict separation between the three fields. Much mischief has been caused by their not having been kept sufficiently apart.

Methodology

We have called the second part of logic "methodology". The word comes from the Greek words "μετά" – "along" – and "ὁδός" – "way". So that it means literally "a λόγος", that is "a speaking of the (right) going-along-the-way". The method is the manner of proceeding in any particular field, that is of organizing activity and of coordinating its objectives. Methodology is the theory of method.

There can be a methodology for every field: there is for example a chemical, a didactic, an ascetic and many other methodologies. They can be divided into two classes: those which discuss respectively the techniques of physical and of intellectual activity. Only the second kind interests us here – although it should be observed in this connection that the methodology of scientific research also includes instructions for physical activities in some fields, e.g. archaeology, chemistry, anatomy etc.

In the domain of intellectual activity it is again possible to distinguish between various classes of method. We are concerned here exclusively with *methods of thought,* that is with directions for correct thinking. The methodology in question, i.e. the science of correct thinking, obviously relates to serious thinking, that is to the acquisition of knowledge. But not all methods of serious thought will concern us here. We shall leave out of account the methods of so-called practical thought, for example of the theory of management, or strategy, and confine ourselves to *theoretical* thought. The difference between the two lies in the fact that practical thought always refers directly to something which the thinker can *do:* the intention is admittedly to achieve a piece of knowledge, but only the knowledge of *how* this or that can be done. Theoretical thought, on the contrary, has no such intentions: it refers exclusively to states of affairs which it wishes to comprehend, quite apart from whether or not these facts can in any way be turned to account.

There are special methods for every sphere of theoretical thought and therefore special methodologies as well. These will sometimes be dealt with within the body of science. But there is also a *general methodology* of theoretical thought: it deals with methods which find application either in all theoretical thinking or at least in a large proportion of the sciences. This and only this methodology is a part of logic – and it alone will be treated here. It is the general methodology of scientific thought.

Science

The word "science" has, among others, two closely coordinated but different meanings: it can be understood either in a subjective or in an objective sense.

(1) Understood subjectively science is nothing but *systematic knowledge.* It is (a) a kind of knowledge, and therefore a quality of the human – and what is more of the individual – subject. A person who has mastered science has the *ability* to understand much of what is covered by it and to carry out correctly the (intellectual) activities belonging to this field. Thus, for example, a person who has mastered arithmetic is able to understand the laws of arithmetic and to perform arithmetical calculations correctly. Science in this sense is nothing but such an ability – and it is of course bound up with real knowledge, i.e. in our example with the knowledge of many laws. Moreover, science in this subjective

sense is (b) *systematic* knowledge. It is not the case that everybody who knows something about a particular field has mastered the science in question, but only the person who has investigated the field systematically, and who knows, over and above the individual states of affairs, how they hang together.

One sometimes speaks of scientific activities, for example of research. Such activities are called "scientific" because their aim consists in the formation or development of science in the subjective sense. So that anyone who does research, or studies, etc., is making an effort to acquire systematic knowledge.

(2) Understood objectively science is not a kind of knowledge but rather a structure of objective propositions. In this sense one says, for example, "Mathematics teaches", or "We borrow from astronomy the proposition . . ." etc. Science thus understood obviously does not exist "in itself" – but it is also not restricted to an individual person. It is rather a social entity, in that it consists of the thinking of a number of persons – none of whom, very often, knows all the propositions belonging to it. Science understood in this objective sense has the following characteristics:

(a) It is a *systematically organized* structure of objective propositions – corresponding to the systematic character of science in the subjective sense.

(b) Not all the propositions belonging to its field belong to a science, but only those which are *known* by at least one person. Or to put it more exactly: apart from propositions which are known there are no real propositions, but only possible ones. Science consists not of possible propositions, but of propositions which have actually been formulated. It is thus possible to speak of the development and progress of science. This comes about through man's perceiving new states of affairs and formulating new propositions in accordance with them.

(c) Science is, as we have said, a *social* undertaking. Therefore only such propositions pertain to it as have been objectivized in some way, i.e. represented by signs, so that they are at any rate in principle accessible to other people. One might admittedly also conceive of an individual science developed by a single person and known only to him; he would not need to represent it in signs. But in fact there is no such science.

Science and Logic

It follows from our description of science that it is inescapably dependent on logic, and this in various senses.

As far as science understood objectively is concerned it is clear that it must be constructed logically. For it is after all constructed systematically, i.e. its propositions stand in logical relations to one another. In its early stages, admittedly, science often amounts to nothing more than a mass of unrelated propositions; this however is regarded by all scientists as unsatisfactory, and the leading motive for research is not only the discovery of new facts but also (and perhaps primarily) the logical ordering of propositions already established. Logic – and furthermore in this case formal logic – therefore forms the indispensable framework for science so understood, which must always presuppose logic.

Logic is similarly a presupposition of science subjectively understood. For this kind of science is first of all systematic knowledge, which consists in the understanding of science in the objective sense. The judgements which constitute this knowledge must therefore be interrelated as much as the propositions of objective science.

If this is so, however, research must also be guided by logic, in two ways: (1) Firstly, of course, the investigator must not only not violate the laws of logic but he must proceed in accordance with these laws. For the acquisition of scientific knowledge is in most cases indirect, that is, inferential. Formal logic is therefore an indispensable presupposition of scientific research. (2) Furthermore research must proceed "methodically": and this means that certain correct methods have to be applied. Such methods are developed in every science according to its particular subject-matter. But all research needs certain general methodical principles, which are applicable to all – or at any rate to many different – sciences. These general methodical principles are discussed in methodology, which, as has been said, forms a part of logic. Hence research, on this account, presupposes logic in the wider sense of the word.

This is not to be taken as meaning that the investigator must learn formal logic or methodology before embarking on his research. On the contrary, we know that in the preliminary stages of a science neither need be known – a natural talent is sufficient. It is also a fact that the principles of logic are first formulated and abstracted from the sciences when these are fairly advanced. Nevertheless two points remain: (1) *every* science, even when the scientist does not do this deliberately, is constructed according to logical and methodological principles; (2) a careful formulation of these principles is usually necessary in the later phases of the development of a science. "Natural logic" is sufficient for simpler matters; it usually fails when things become more complicated. But it fails regularly and completely when one tries to give an account of the philosophical meaning of what has been achieved: for this an intimate knowledge of formal logic and methodology is absolutely necessary.

Division of the Work

After what has been said one might imagine that general methodology has to do exclusively with the indirect acquisition of knowledge. But this is not the case. Even in the domain of the direct acquisition of knowledge there are certain methods which have now been developed technically and form the subject-matter of general methodology. Among these the *phenomenological* occupies an important place. It is a method of intellectual observation and of the description of what is observed. But it comprises many rules which apply quite generally to all kinds of thinking. It is furthermore one of the most recent methods, one which is not only used today by about a half of contemporary philosophers but which is employed outside philosophy as well in various intellectual disciplines, and seems to be meeting with ever greater recognition. Logic is closely connected with it, in its third part, the philosophy of logic. We shall deal first of all with the phenomenological method.

In recent times three groups of indirect methods have been elaborated. The first has to do with the indirect knowledge which consists in the interpretation of a language. Because of the prime importance of language in many sciences (above all in historical sciences, but also in mathematical ones) the *analysis of language* belongs to the general theory of method. It forms to some extent a counterpart to the phenomenological method: it also is concerned with the analysis of things, but in a completely different, indirect way, by means of a structure of signs.

We shall also be concerned with inference proper. Two kinds of inference will be introduced in this connection: *deductive* and *reductive*. (The meaning of these expressions will be given later).

The work will therefore be divided as follows:
1. The phenomenological method.
2. The analysis of language.
3. The deductive method.
4. The reductive method.

CHAPTER II

THE PHENOMENOLOGICAL METHOD

3. GENERAL REMARKS

Historical Preliminaries

The name "phenomenology" appears to have been used for the first time by Johann Heinrich Lambert in his *Neues Organon* (1764). The word also occurs in Kant (*Metaphysische Anfangsgrunde der Naturwissenschaft*, 1786), Hegel (*Phänomenologie des Geistes*, 1807), Renouvier (*Fragments de la philosophie de Sir W. Hamilton*, 1840), Hamilton (*Lectures on Logic*, 1860), Amiel (*Journal intime*, 1869), E. von Hartmann (*Phänomenologie des sittlichen Bewußtseins*, 1879), and in other works. The meaning attached to it has differed very greatly from one writer to another, but none of these early writers used it to denote a precisely circumscribed method of thought.

Edmund Husserl (1859–1938) was the first to use the word "phenomenology" in this sense. His methodological ideas have exerted a decisive influence on European and to some extent also on American philosophy. Between the two World Wars an important school of philosophy gathered around him (Scheler, Ingarden, Farber, Stein, Becker, Fink, Pfänder, Koyré and others). Later on, his method was adopted, with certain modifications, by the existentialist philosophers, and it now constitutes the most important procedure used by this school (Marcel, Heidegger, Sartre, Merleau-Ponty). And since intellectual disciplines in general are being deeply influenced by existentialism in various countries, especially Germany, France and Italy, the phenomenological method has become of great importance for these disciplines also. A few independent thinkers, such as N. Hartmann, also use a kind of phenomenological method. It is therefore no exaggeration to say that at any rate on the European continent the phenomenological method is of decisive significance in philosophy. In North American and English philosophy, on the other hand, it is not much used.

Methodological Preliminaries

It is not easy to expound the principles which are basic for the phenomeno-logical method of Husserl himself. For Husserl developed this method gradually, in the course of his philosophical inquiries, and never supplied a concise account of it. There are only occasional methodological obser-vations in his writings, and they are not always easy to understand. Furthermore, Husserl used the word "phenomenology" to denote a doctrine as well as a method. It is true that no method can be wholly divorced from certain presuppositions in the actual content of the thought, but in this case the intertwining of method and content is so close that if often appears doubtful whether a purely methodological idea can be distinguished at all.

The following distinction is, however, of fundamental importance. An essential feature of the phenomenological method is the so-called *process of reduction*. In Husserl there are to be found two stages of reduction, one "eidetic" and one "phenomenological" in the narrower sense. *Eidetic* reduction was worked out by Husserl principally in his *Logische Unter-suchungen* (1901), while he turned towards *phenomenological* reduction, in the narrower sense, increasingly from the *Ideen* (1913) onwards. Here we shall deal only with the first, or eidetic, kind of reduction, leaving phe-nomenological reduction out of account, since it is so bound up with Husserl's own special doctrines that it can hardly be considered a method of any general significance.

Essential Characteristics of Phenomenology

The phenomenological method is a special cognitive procedure. It consists essentially in an intellectual observation of the object, i.e. it is based on *intuition*. This intuition refers to the given; the leading rule of phenome-nology is "back to the things themselves", where by "things" is meant just the given. This however requires a threefold exclusion or "reduction", also called *"ἐποχή"*: first, of all subjectivity: what is called for is a purely *objective* standpoint, concentrated singlemindedly on the object; second, of all theoretical knowledge, such as hypotheses and proofs derived from other sources, so that *only the given* will be admitted; third, of all *tradition*, i.e. of everything that others have taught about the object in question.

The given object ("phenomenon") has, in its turn, to be subjected to a twofold reduction: first, the *existence* of the thing must be disregarded, (and attention concentrated exclusively on *what* the object is, on its "whatness"; second, everything inessential has to be excluded from this "whatness", and only the the essence of the object analysed.

In this connection it should be noted that the phenomenological reduction is not the same thing as a denial. The elements excluded are only set aside, and abstracted from while attention is concentrated on what remains. The eidetic reduction similarly does not imply a value-judgement on the aspects that are excluded: to use the phenomenological method does not rule out the possibility of using other methods later on and of considering the aspects that have been ignored for the time being. The rule of reduction is valid only for the duration of the phenomenological exercise.

Justification of the Phenomenological Method

At first sight phenomenological observation seems to be something quite simple, and to consist merely in keeping one's intellectual eyes open, and where appropriate putting oneself in a suitable position for getting a good view of the object by making various external movements. A special method for regulating the movement of thought itself seems at first to be quite unnecessary.

But it is necessary, and for two reasons. (1) Man is so constituted that he has an almost incorrigible disposition to see, in what he looks at, extraneous elements which are not contained in the object itself at all. These extraneous elements are either introduced into what is actually seen by our subjective emotional attitude (thus a coward sees the enemy's strength as twice what it actually is), or they are put into the object by knowledge acquired elsewhere. We project into the given object our own hypotheses, ideas, theories etc. Now the whole point of the eidetic reduction is to see the given object and nothing else at all. To attain this it is necessary to apply a carefully developed method. (2) No object is simple: every object is infinitely complex, consisting as it does of various components and aspects which are not all equally important. Man cannot grasp all these elements at once – he has to consider them one after the other. This too requires a carefully devised method.

For these reasons not only *is* there a phenomenological method, but also it is *necessary* to master it in order to see correctly.

17

So, at least, the phenomenologists themselves maintain. Their stand-point is disputed by empiricists and Kantians. But apart from the im-portance of this controversy, a chapter on phenomenological method must be included even in a brief exposition of contemporary methods of thought, since it is used by many (possibly even most) present-day philosophers and contains many principles which are valid independently of any particular philosophical point of view. Almost all the rules of the phenomenological method might even be represented as general scientific rules, though to do so would run counter to the intentions of the phenome-nologists themselves. All the same, the objective fact remains that they have formulated universally valid rules for theoretical thought.

4. "BACK TO THE THINGS THEMSELVES"

The Observation of Essence

The main principle of the phenomenological method, referred to above, which consists in "going back to the things themselves", means first of all that one has to *see* these things, in an intellectual sense. The phenome-nological method is a method of intuition, of intellectual observation. According to the phenomenologists an observation of this kind is the necessary foundation of all true cognition. In the terminology of Husserl, *the primordial dator consciousness is the only legitimate source of knowledge.* For every indirect acquisition of knowledge, every deduction, is a de-duction from something, and this something must in the last analysis be observable. It is, however, only possible to observe that which is given. This, the "thing", is what Husserl calls the "phenomenon", from the Greek φαινόμενον, what appears, or lies clearly before us (φῶς = light). The observation itself, however, is an (inward, intellectual) articulation of the phenomenon, as in the Greek λέγειν. Hence the term "phenome-nology"; it is an articulation of what is given, and of what is given directly in intellectual observation.

In this connection it must be observed: (1) Intuition is interpreted as the opposite of the discursive acquisition of knowledge as well as of abstraction. Here we use the term only in the first sense; that is, we understand by "intuition" a direct, but *not* a complete, grasp of the object. Human cognition is essentially abstractive: it embraces only certain aspects of what is given and is unable to exhaust everything which is there presented. There is no such thing as intuition in the sense of exhaustive cognition, not at any rate for human beings. (2) Phenomenologists are sometimes criticized, and perhaps not wholly without reason, for wanting to exclude every other form of knowledge, for example the knowledge of probabilities. Their principles, however, do not really lead to any such consequences. The knowledge that something is probable is obviously only too frequent, but it is still knowledge. If, therefore, a statement is made only as a probability, the person who makes it must *know* that the statement is probable. The probability of a statement can be known only by inference, and such inference always presupposes the certainty of something and thus the grasping of certain objects. The basic theory of phenomenology is valid in this and only in this sense. If it were taken as meaning that we could know only certainties it would obviously be false.

Objectivism

The second main rule of the phenomenological method, as propounded by Husserl himself, may be formulated as follows: In all enquiry thought should be concentrated exclusively on the object, to the complete elimination of everything subjective. Put in this way the rule is an essential constituent of Western scientific method. It contains two different though closely allied practical principles.

To begin with, it requires that the investigator should devote himself completely to the object of the enquiry, having regard only for what is objective. He must exclude everything that comes from himself, from the subject, above all his own feelings, desires, personal attitudes, etc. What is required of him is a detached observation of the object, a pure theoretical approach, in the original Greek sense of the word "theory" (observation). The researcher who acts in accordance with this rule is a pure knowing essence, one who forgets himself completely.

Secondly, the rule requires a contemplative attitude, i.e. the exclusion of utilitarian considerations. The scientist must not ask himself what purpose this or that might serve, but purely and simply how it *is*. Nevertheless, the practical sphere, for example the moral and the religious, can itself be investigated phenomenologically, as can be seen in the work of Scheler and Otto, but in this case the practical object – purpose, value, and the like – is examined from a purely contemplative standpoint.

Phenomenology is thoroughly theoretical, in the sense that it has no practical end in view.

Needless to say the objectivism to which phenomenologists aspire is only an ideal. Man is not made of intellect alone; even in science emotional motives are always more or less involved. Some such motives even seem to be beneficial to research, as for example the passionate desire for knowledge. For the rest, however, feelings and emotions only too often mar the purity of scientific observation. It seems practically impossible to exclude them altogether; but this only enhances the importance of the phenomenological rule. A deliberate effort has to be made to keep to it – otherwise it is all too easy to succumb to subjectivism. As the phenomenologists rightly point out, we owe the tremendous achievements of Western civilization precisely to objectivism.

The Subjective Thought of Kierkegaard

This long-established rule of objectivism, newly enunciated and strengthened by the work of Husserl, is resisted by existentialist philosophers, the followers of Sören Kierkegaard. They maintain that objectivism is an inadequate principle on which to base philosophical investigation; in their view the philosopher, the "subjective thinker", ought on the contrary to be "concerned". Gabriel Marcel endeavours to repeat to himself every day: *"Je ne suis pas au spectacle"*. Many existentialist philosophers similarly regard purely theoretic thinking as worthless. They often even go so far as to maintain that all genuinely philosophical thinking is without an object, since it refers to so-called existence (human *Dasein*) which is precisely not an object, but a subject.

On closer examination these assertions of the continental philosophers, which are very popular at present, prove to be less revolutionary than might at first appear.

(1) To begin with, it has to be noted that the word "object" is ambiguous. According to Husserl, the "object" is everything that is given, everything that is contemplated. The existentialist philosophers, on the other hand, take the word quite literally: for them the object is that which confronts the I *(Gegenstand ist, was dem Ich gegenübersteht)*. In this sense the I (the so-called existence) can of course not be an object. But if we contemplate existence, it is nevertheless an object in the original phenomenological sense, since an object is anything about which we

speak. We talk about existence, and consequently it has become an object for us. Furthermore, the existentialist philosophers consider existence something that is never finished, something that has no clear outline, whereas an object is definite and tangible. For this reason, too, they cannot regard existence as an "object". In the original phenomenological terminology, however, the object was not defined at all, hence existence can also be called an object. It is all simply a matter of words.

(2) When existentialist philosophers regard fear or anxiety as a necessary condition for the understanding of existence they clearly mean that the particular object which I myself am (my existence) is best revealed when I am in this kind of emotional state. This may be so, but that is not to say that true investigation is possible when the investigator is ridden with anxiety. Sartre's work *Being and Nothingness*, for example, leaves no room for doubt that its author performed this prodigious intellectual task in a wholly contemplative state, coolly and scientifically. Perhaps anxiety was a pre-condition of the investigation, but it could not possibly have helped the work while it was actually being written; on the contrary, it would have made calm analysis impossible.

(3) The object of the method advocated by the existentialist philosophers is human existence, and thus something quite individual. It is true that the existentialists hold that every object is necessarily related to this existence and can be understood only on the basis of a clarification of existence. But this is a thesis which is not universally accepted and certainly does not apply in the natural sciences. So far the natural sciences have managed to deal successfully with the meaning of things without taking account of human existence, and they continue to work in a basically objective way.

As far as that goes, the objective method is applied in quite exemplary fashion in the work of two leading existentialist philosophers, Heidegger and Sartre.

The Exclusion of Theory and Tradition

The rule "back to the things themselves" requires the exclusion not only of all subjective feelings but also of everything objective which is not directly given in the object under examination. This includes everything which we know from other sources or by inference. Only what is given, the phenomenon, must be seen, and beyond that nothing.

21

(1) First the rule requires that all theories, deductions, hypotheses etc. should be excluded. This does not mean that the phenomenologists dismiss the indirect acquisition of knowledge as altogether worthless; they are quite prepared to allow it, but only *after* the phenomenological groundwork has been laid. This constitutes the absolute beginning; among other things it provides the basis for the validity of rules of deduction, so that the use of indirect methods in the course of phenomenological investigations cannot be permitted.

(2) The exclusion of tradition is closely connected with this point. What is involved is not merely the principle, already enunciated emphatically by Thomas Aquinas, according to which reference to human authority constitutes the weakest argument, so that what is asserted by others must never be relied on as a sure foundation. The phenomenological method requires not merely a strict application of this Thomist principle but, in addition, that the whole "state of knowledge" should be excluded, whether it has been tested by the investigator or not. Only things, i.e. phenomena, exactly as they stand before the intellectual eye of the observer, are to be spoken of; nothing else.

In practice these postulates, like those of pure objectivism, are uncommonly difficult, indeed impossible, to fulfil absolutely. In the human mind seeing is so bound up with inference that we have the utmost difficulty in keeping them apart. Quite involuntarily we project into the object our earlier acquired knowledge. The art of pure contemplation can only be learned by a long course of training.

Let me illustrate the principle by two examples from my own seminar work. A student who was asked to describe a red spot phenomenologically began as follows: "I see a red spot on the board. This spot consists of tiny particles of red chalk..." That statement is already non-phenomenological. The student knew that the red spot consisted of particles of chalk because he had seen the professor making the spot with the chalk; the chalk was not *given* in the object itself. Another example: a student offered the following analysis of the sense of duty: "the sense of duty arises in our consciousness when certain complicated physiological processes occur in the brain". Phenomenologically speaking, this is clearly quite wrong. Man has never seen his own brain, still less the physiological processes which are supposed to occur in the brain. The phenomenon of the sense of duty, as a phenomenon, has nothing at all to do with these physiological processes.

Positive Principles of the Observation of Essence

It might be thought that observation was itself such a simple process that no particular rules were necessary and that it would be enough to keep the eyes of the mind open in order to see the object correctly. But this is not the case. We have already mentioned some negative rules of the phenomenological method: if the investigator is insufficiently trained in the art of observation, or even if he is not sufficiently careful to restrict his attention to that which lies before him, he will project subjective elements, theories, traditional points of view, and the like, into the object. There are, however, some positive rules. They may be stated as follows:

(1) It is imperative to see *everything* that is given, as far as that is possible. This rule, clear and simple in itself, must be explicitly formulated and deliberately applied because there is a strong tendency to see only some aspects of what is given. Uexküll has shown that animals only take in what is vitally important for them; and in this man has much in common with the animals. What he has in addition consists, among other things, in his ability to acquire theoretical, non-practical knowledge. But in spite of this, we are all too prone to be blind to certain elements in what is given. The first task of phenomenological investigation is therefore the disclosure of phenomena which have been overlooked.

(2) Further, phenomenological observation must be *descriptive*. That is to say, the object must be taken apart, and its elements then described and analysed. For every object is infinitely complex. The clearer the observation, the better the elements can be differentiated and understood in relation to one another. Heidegger calls this kind of analysis "exegesis" *(Auslegung)* or "hermeneutics". It must be carefully noted, however, that such phenomenological hermeneutics is not to be mistaken for reduction (which will be dealt with later, in Section 5); here it is a matter of the direct, but there of the indirect, acquisition of knowledge.

5. THE OBJECT OF PHENOMENOLOGICAL INVESTIGATION

The Phenomenon

The object of phenomenological observation and exegesis is called the "phenomenon" by Husserl and his followers. But this word has other distinct meanings, apart from the phenomenological, which we shall discuss briefly in order to avoid misunderstanding.

(1) In the first place, the "phenomenon" is often contrasted with "reality"; it is taken to be an *appearance*. This has nothing whatever to do with the phenomenological sense of the word. Whether what is given is "real" or "only apparent" plays no part in the phenomenologists' considerations. For them the only important thing is that they should be dealing with something plainly given.

(2) Further, the phenomenon as *appearance* is often contrasted with the "thing in itself". In this sense the thing shows itself through the phenomenon, in much the same way as illness shows itself through fever. This also is not what the phenomenologists have in mind. They are not in the least interested in some possible "thing in itself" lying behind the phenomenon: they want only to observe the phenomenon itself, the given.

(3) In the natural sciences the word "phenomenon" is used to indicate processes which permit of direct observation by the senses. This meaning is much narrower than the one which phenomenologists give to the word, since in the first place, according to them, it is not at all necessary to be able to observe the phenomenon with the senses (as we shall see later, it is enough if the phenomenon is imagined) and in the second place it need not be a process; while phenomenologists can investigate processes too, they deal above all with structures.

The sense of the word "phenomenon" here is, then, in the words of Heidegger: *the thing showing itself as itself,* that which is itself, and truly shows itself to be what lies clearly before us.

The Exclusion of Existence

The exclusions mentioned so far (of the subjective, of the theoretical, and of tradition) are not yet enough. An authentically phenomenological method demands also the exclusion of the existence of the object. It is a matter of indifference whether the object really exists or not, its existence does not enter into the question. If, for example, somebody undertakes a phenomenological investigation of a red spot, it does not matter whether or not there is such a thing as a red spot in the world.

In this lies one of the fundamental differences between the phenomenological and the empirical method. In the latter the observer proceeds from the ascertaining of facts, that is, he first convinces himself that such-and-such is *factually* the case. He ascertains, for example, that this or that amount of water really did exist in a particular place and at a particular time. In the phenomenological process, on the other hand, there is no such ascertaining. Facts in this case have no significance.

A misgiving may arise here: how, if this is the case, is it possible to speak of what is *given* in phenomenology? What is given certainly seems to be what really exists. To this it must be said that ultimately every object must exist, or at least be grounded in something existent, in order to be given. But it does not follow from this that phenomenology is bound to deal with the existence of the object. For even if the object does exist, its existence can be ignored and only the fact that it is *what* it is considered, and this the phenomenologists do; it is also possible to deal with objects which are merely imagined.

Essence

The real object of phenomenological enquiry is essence, the εἶδος. This word too has several meanings, which must be briefly fixed in order to understand the special sense in which it is used by the phenomenologists.

(1) The word "essence" often occurs in such phrases as "man is mortal essence".* Here "essence" means more or less the same as "thing"; although admittedly it has to be a living thing. In phenomenological usage "essence" never refers to things of this sort, such as human beings. "Essence" refers only to aspects, certain elements, contained in such things.

(2) We also speak of the "essence *of* a thing", for example, the "essence of life". This also is not the meaning given to the word by phenome-

---

* *Translator's note: Wesen,* here translated "essence", means in ordinary language "being", and is often so translated; in some contexts it also means "creature". Strictly speaking, however, *Wesen* is essential being as opposed to existential *(Dasein* or *Existenz)*, these representing complementary modes of Being in general *(Sein)*. In this section what is important is to stress the phenomenological aspect of being, the essential nature of things as given, in contrast to its ontological aspect, and for this purpose the word "essence" has acquired, in English translations of Husserl and other phenomenologists, a technical meaning which makes it the only possible choice as an equivalent for *Wesen*. Some of the ambiguities of *Wesen* in German, however, are not reflected in corresponding ambiguities of "essence" in English, and this fact may explain why these paragraphs, whose intention is to clear up difficulties in German, translate rather awkwardly into English.

nologists. While the essence of life is very difficult to grasp, the phenomenological essence lies clearly before the observer; it is not in any way a
"hidden essence", but on the contrary a phenomenon, something which
reveals itself.

(3) Essence in the phenomenological sense must be carefully distinguished from the Aristotelian εἶδος. The phenomenological concept
is more comprehensive. In addition to his εἶδος Aristotle recognizes
other determining properties (ἴδια) necessarily connected with it. Phenomenology, on the other hand, comprises everything that necessarily
coheres in the phenomenon under the term "essence", which includes
the Aristotelian properties.

The phenomenological essence therefore excludes two kinds of factor:
existence (Dasein), and everything *contingent*. One might call this essence
the fundamental structure of the object. Only "structure" must not be
thought of as a mere texture of relationships; rather the word must be
applied to the whole underlying content, including qualities, etc.

Essence and Meaning

In order further to clarify the concept of essence we shall outline briefly
the position of the empiricists, who deny essence, and indicate the phenomenological attitude to these views.

According to the empiricists essence is relative. What is essential to a
thing from one point of view may be inessential from another. In a
wooden triangle, for example, someone who is interested in geometry
will consider only its geometrical characteristics as essential, and will
therefore say that for this object only the three sides and the three angles
are essential, while the fact that it is made of wood, or that it is so
many centimeters long, is inessential and of no consequence. For another observer, on the other hand, who is interested in the material
rather than the geometrical properties of the triangle, its being made of
wood will be essential, but its geometrical form, the three sides and the
three angles, will be inessential. It might be remarked that the word
"triangle" means a three-sided figure with three angles in any case. But
this objection would not disconcert the empiricists, who lay stress on the
word "mean": for them essence is, as can be seen in this example, what
is meant by a word, and only that; essence is nothing else than verbal
meaning. And since all meanings are relative – the same word can be

used at will to denote many different things – the essence of an object is a relative concept; what is essential for one observer may be quite inessential for another. Everything depends on the meaning which we arbitrarily give to words. In things themselves there is no essence, all the aspects of a thing are intrinsically of equal value. Man introduces, through his conventions, the distinction between the essential and the inessential, in that he assigns meanings to words.

This line of thought is rejected by the phenomenologists as unsatisfactory. It is certainly admitted that the meanings of words are relative and also that it is true that we may concentrate on one aspect of a thing on one occasion – for example, its geometrical form – and on another aspect on another occasion – for example, its material constitution. But just these aspects are regarded by the phenomenologists as "objects": for example, being-made-of-wood is such an object. This has, in itself and quite independently of the name we give to it, certain necessary properties. For instance, everything made of wood is extended and occupies space, not because we call it "wooden" but because it is so constituted. If we were to say "spirit" instead of "wood", this new name of the object would not make the slightest difference to its structure: it would still be material and occupy space. But while geometrical form is inessential to a wooden object, and has no connection with what it is called, for a triangle (i.e. what we normally call a triangle) this form is essential. The relativity of possible points of view consists therefore in nothing more than the possibility of concentrating on different objects, and has nothing at all to do with our problem. In this connection the relativity of the meanings of words is just as unimportant.

The Phenomenology of Existence

From what has been said so far it may seem odd that most of the present-day followers of Husserl concern themselves with existence. The word has, however, a narrower meaning among the existentialists, with whom Husserl's students are associated, than among other philosophers, since it denotes human existence only. But this is understood quite explicitly as *Dasein*, that is – in an apparent reversal of Husserl's own procedure – its nature or essence is excluded from consideration. At any rate this is the procedure these philosophers claim to follow. But if we examine more closely how they really proceed it is clear that fundamentally they have hardly diverged from Husserl's point of view at all. In particular the following points must be made.

(1) They deal with what is given, with the phenomenon, and wish in principle to exclude all indirect acquisition of knowledge from their enquiries. It is true that they do not claim their method to be one of observation, but since an emotional state can at most create a disposition to knowledge, never being able to produce the genuine article, the intellectual action which ultimately takes place must be a kind of observation, whatever it may be called.

(2) The object of their enquiry, the human existence referred to above, is described and interpreted in a genuinely phenomenological sense. Heidegger has, as was mentioned earlier, provided the best theoretical exposition of this interpretation, the sub-title of Sartre's main work is *Essai d'une ontologie phénomenologique,* and Marcel has written a *Phenomenology of Having.* These philosophers do in fact apply the method of phenomenological analysis to their object.

(3) Such analyses always show that existence possesses what these philosophers call a "structure". Heidegger has even introduced a special name for the elements of this structure: he calls them *"Existentiale".* The detailed discussion of existence occupies a considerable part of the works of the existentialists.

(4) Although they always maintain that they are only concerned with what Heidegger calls the *je-meinige,* that which occurs only once, it is clear that what the existentialists believe themselves to have discovered belongs to every human existence. It is not simply a structure of this existence, but a *necessary* structure.

The achievement of the existentialists consists in the demonstration that it is possible to find an essence in existence itself. An important contemporary philosopher has expressed this by saying that the existentialists are extremists among philosophers of essence. At any rate their treatment of human existence remains entirely within the framework of the phenomenological method.

On the Newer "Deeper" Phenomenology

Husserl himself, but even more many of his successors, have been mainly interested in the so-called "constitution" of the object. They have attempted to discover pre-objective objects, if the expression may be allowed; in most cases what is involved is a proof *that* man produces his objects in one way or another, and an explanation of *how* he does this. At the same time – at least on the part of a considerable number of these thinkers – methods are used which have not the slightest connection with the simple early Husserlian observation. From this standpoint everything that has been said here would be regarded as elementary, and perhaps even as pre-philosophical and pre-phenomenological.

This, however, is a quite specialized approach, although it is widespread among the philosophers of continental Europe. No authentic special science, and no philosopher who does not belong to this school, will be able to recognize or use these methods. But our concern is with *general* methods of thought. In view of this the problems posed by the new phenomenology need not be discussed here.

CHAPTER III

SEMIOTIC METHODS

6. GENERAL REMARKS

Methodological Preliminaries

The inclusion of this chapter on language in an exposition of contemporary methods of thought will be justified in what follows. First two methodological points will be briefly touched upon.

One might ask why the discussion of linguistic problems should follow closely upon that of phenomenological method. The reason is that the analysis of language, while it is not unimportant even in connection with the direct acquisition of knowledge, is very important indeed in the case of knowledge acquired indirectly, since in this case the object is not given and the movement of thought is usually quite complicated, rendering precise symbolization essential. As will be seen, processes crop up in which an understanding of the use of language is absolutely indispensable. For this reason, while semiotic methods *may* be discussed after phenomenological ones, they *must* be taken up before any of the other methods.

Another far more difficult question is that of knowing how to distinguish between the province of semiotic and that of deductive logic. According to certain philosophical schools, especially that of the logical empiricists, logic and the analysis of language are the same thing. Even if one does not share this extreme view it is often difficult to tell them apart. As early a writer as Aristotle subsumed his semiotic (the first five chapters of his treatise *On Rhetoric*) under his logic. In any case the distinction is bound to be to some extent arbitrary and relative from the methodological point of view, quite apart from the fundamental philosophical position which may be adopted. Here it will be dealt with as follows: everything which is concerned with the *correctness* of statements will be treated in the chapter on deduction, and everything having to do with the *meaning (Sinn)* of expressions will be treated in the chapter on semiotic.

Historical Preliminaries

Aristotle was the first to deal with semiotic problems systematically – his work *On Rhetoric* contains among other things the first known system of syntactic categories – although Plato and the Sophists (Cratylus, etc.) had already touched upon them incidentally. The subject then underwent a significant development at the hands of the Stoics and Scholastics, in the latter case principally in the *Grammaticae speculativae.* Unfortunately the works of the Stoics, with the exception of a few fragments, have been lost, and scholastic semiotic has so far hardly been investigated. So-called "modern" times can claim little progress in the field, the development of mathematical logic having only just brought with it some new research of this kind. Husserl (who, it must be admitted, was no mathematical logician) carried through important semiotic analyses in his *Logical Investigations,* while Frege reconstructed and partly extended the ideas of the early Stoics. Recent research is associated primarily with the metamathematics of Hilbert. The most important contemporary workers in the field are Tarski (1935) and Carnap (1937). The name "semiotic", like the general classification of this branch of learning, is due to Charles Morris (1938). Today semiotic is being actively studied and developed, thanks partly to the stimulus of other sciences, principally physics, which require a much more exact analysis of language than hitherto. Also the general outlook of the logical empiricists, who consider linguistic analysis the sole object of philosophy, has furthered the development substantially.

General Justification of Linguistic Analysis

Signs, the object of semiotic, have become important, indeed necessary, to scientific method, for several reasons:

(1) Science is a collective undertaking which achieves results only through the cooperation of many workers over a period of time. But such cooperation requires the communication of knowledge, and this is effected by signs, especially by spoken and written words. Words are therefore not merely accessories, but an essential instrument of science.

(2) Words are substantial, material things, or events. Given their

success in the clear formulation of concepts the work of the scientist is considerably facilitated, even apart from the question of cooperation. The human mind is so constituted that it works most easily with material things, and comprehends them best. One has only to think of counting: it can be done quite well "in the head", but much more simply and surely with the aid of written symbols.

(3) There is finally yet a third reason why words are so important for knowledge. The expression of thought by means of signs is a kind of artistic activity. Now it is a well-known fact that, while the artist's production is normally guided by an idea, this idea is usually quite inadequate to the finished work. The idea is elaborated and refined during the course of the material production itself. This is often the case in verbal expression: the concept which is to be communicated by means of the words often achieves completeness and precision only in the process of expression. Here the fact that words not only serve as the vehicle for concepts, but can also have an autonomous function of their own, is not taken into account. Even as means of expression they are clearly of the greatest importance.

If words are indispensable for knowledge, they can also be dangerous; they can easily lead to misunderstandings not only between different people but also in the work of a single person: a word may be taken as the adequate expression of a concept, and turn out not to be so at all, or its meaning may conceal something which leads the investigator in the wrong direction.

The Three Dimensions of the Sign

The main idea of semiotics, which is also the basis of its subdivision, may be set out as follows. When a man says something to another, every word he uses refers to three distinct objects:

(a) First of all the word belongs to a language, and this means that it bears a certain relationship to the other words of this language. For example, it may stand between two other words in a sentence (as in the case of the word "and"), or at the beginning of a sentence, and so on. These relationships are called *syntactic*, and link words to one another.

(b) Second, what the man says has a *significance:* his words *mean* something, they are intended to convey something definite to the other person. In addition to the syntactic relationship, we have therefore to deal with another relationship, that of the word to what it is intended to mean. This relationship is called *semantic*.

(c) Finally, the word is spoken by a particular person and directed to a particular person. There is therefore a third kind of relationship, that between the word and the persons who use it. These relationships are called *pragmatic*.

These various relationships are interconnected in a special way. The pragmatic relationship presupposes the semantic and the syntactic, and the semantic presupposes the syntactic. A meaningless word is of no service to human understanding, and in order to have a meaning it must have certain relationships to other words. On the other hand, the syntactic relationship does not presuppose the semantic and pragmatic, and the semantic relationship may be studied without reference to the pragmatic. It would be possible to build a complete syntax even for a completely meaningless language; we could, for example, form a simple language in which only the signs P and x occurred and in which it would be a syntactic rule that P always preceded x; there would be no need to know what P or x actually meant.

The connection between the three types of relationship is like that

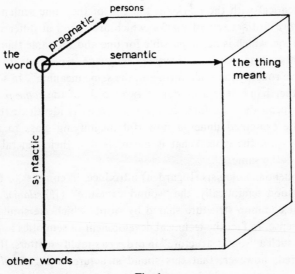

Fig. 1

which exists between the three dimensions of a geometrical body. The whole phenomenon of the word is like a three-dimensional body; we can isolate either of the first two kinds of relationship (the syntactic and the semantic) or a single one (the syntactic) only by abstraction, just as a surface or a straight line is isolated from a geometrical body. This comparison is best explained by the accompanying diagram.

The Semiotic Concept of the Word

At the outset of these remarks special attention must be drawn to the fact that the word with which semiotics is concerned is the material word, that is, in the case of the spoken word, a set of waves in the air, and in the case of the written word, a series of ink-marks on paper. That the word has to be taken in this sense is already clear from the fact that it is set over against what it means. This observation is important because "word" is used with a different meaning in everyday language.

One important result of this view is that we can never use the same word twice in one statement, let alone in several statements. Let us take for example the simple statement of identity: "Fritz is Fritz". According to the semiotic conception we have here a series of ink-marks. The marks which we read as "Fritz" at the beginning of the sentence are by no means identical with the marks at the end of the same sentence, since they are *two* distinct sets of marks, which are found at different places on the paper, which is never possible for one and the same thing. When we say "the same word" in everyday language, we mean "two words which have roughly the same form and the same meaning". In semiotics, on the other hand, it is a matter of *two* words of the *same form*. This does not mean that the form of the two words is identical; they have only to be examined under a powerful magnifying glass to establish that this is not the case. What is meant is that their general graphic structure is the same.

Some phenomenologists (Ingarden) introduce, in contrast to the word as understood semiotically, the "sound structure" (*Wortlaut*), i.e. precisely that common structure shared by words which are similar in the semiotic sense. In fact the technical development of semiotics requires an appeal to such a "sound structure" in order to simplify matters. It must be remembered, however, that this sound structure is a *general* notion, and thus something which actually occurs only in individual words, as understood semiotically. It is not a thing, but a property of a thing, of the sign as conceived in the material (semiotic) sence.

7. FORMALISM

Preliminary orientation

One of the most important achievements of modern methodology is the realization that operating with language on the syntactic level can make the work of thought considerably easier. Such a method of operation is called a "formalism". It consists in ignoring every *meaning* of the signs employed and considering the signs exclusively according to their *written form*. If a language is constructed formalistically, it is called a "formalized language"; the term "formalism" simply is sometimes used, but this is misleading and it is more convenient to use the word "formalism" only in describing the method.

In the use of formalism a clear distinction is made between two things. On the one hand we have *language in itself* with its purely syntactic rules, rules, that is, which refer exclusively to the material form of the signs, but never to their meaning; on the other hand we have, at any rate in most cases, an interpretation of the content, an allocation of meaning to the signs. Language in itself and the interpretation of language are to some extent independent. It is true that a syntax must be in existence before interpretation is possible, but the reverse does not hold, since it is easy enough to construct a language without attaching any meaning to it. Such a language we call "formalistic" or "abstract". Different interpretations can usually be applied to the same formalized language.

The interpretation of a language is the concern of semantics, not of syntax, and will be dealt with in a later chapter. As far as syntax is concerned, that is, formalized language, we must, in order to set it forth, solve two problems: (a) first we must enunciate certain rules allowing us to establish unambiguously which signs are admissible, i.e. "meaningful", in this language; (b) second, rules must be established to determine which statements – if the language in question contains statements at all – are well formed. This second task has been traditionally assigned to formal logic and here again we propose to deal with these problems in the fourth chapter. In the case of the first task it is possible to distinguish three groups of problems: one which concerns formalism in general, one which refers to the syntactic meaning of a simple expression, and one which refers to the meaning of expressions in combination with one another. We shall deal briefly with the first group of problems in the next section and with the two others in the succeeding two chapters.

Calculation

Formalism consists essentially in the extension of a method that has been known for centuries, namely that of calculation. It will therefore be appropriate first of all to consider briefly the structure of ordinary arithmetical and algebraic calculation as taught in schools.

(1) A simple arithmetical operation, e.g. multiplication, seems to consist essentially in splitting the problem up into separate parts and solving one part after another. For example, in order to multiply 27 by 35 mentally we proceed somewhat as follows: first we multiply 20×30, then 7×30, then 7×5, etc. There seems to be no question of formalism here. But if we do the multiplication in writing we usually write down the individual results in a definite order, e.g.:

$$27 \times 35$$
$$\overline{}$$
$$135$$
$$81$$
$$\overline{}$$
$$945$$

If we were asked why we wrote the 1 in the second line one place to the left and not under the 5 of the first line, then we should reply after some consideration: because 1 belongs in the tens column and its place is therefore under the digit of the upper number in the tens column. In the act of multiplication, however, we do not think of this explicitly, but simply apply the syntactic rule according to which each stage of the multiplication (that is each new row) has to be moved one place further to the left. To calculate accurately it is not necessary to know why one must proceed in this way, it is quite sufficient to know the relevant syntactic rule (along with a few others, of course).

(2) Let us look at another example, this time from algebra. Take the equation:

$$ax^2 + bx + c = 0.$$

To find the formula for the solution of this equation, we begin by transferring the "c" to the right-hand side, with the opposite sign:

$$ax^2 + bx = -c.$$

Here too it would be easy to explain the reason for this "changing sides", but in fact we do not bother about it at all, proceeding instead quite simply according to the syntactic rule: "Every element on one side of an equation may be transferred to the other side, but it must then be given the opposite sign, that is '$-$' instead of '$+$' or vice versa." In the case of somewhat more complicated calculations we must limit ourselves to the syntactic rule, since our mental capacity simply is not sufficient to think of the reasons for the rule at the same time.

Calculation owes its relative safety not to the fact that it takes place with numbers, but to the formalism. It is an application of formalism to the language of numbers.

Application of Calculation to Non-Mathematical Objects

This same method can now be easily applied to other fields which have nothing whatever to do with numbers. Here is an example from Aristotelian syllogistic logic. As is well known, according to this system, a universal negative statement may be "converted", e.g. the negative statement

"no men are stones"

may be "converted" into the statement

"no stones are men".

In classical logic such a statement is usually represented by the series of signs $S\,e\,P$, in which S stands for the subject, P for the predicate, and the letter e (from the Latin nego) indicates that the statement is a universal negative. If we write our statement in this form, it is easy to establish a purely syntactic rule which corresponds exactly to the principle of the convertibility of such statements. We say therefore: "The letters adjoining e may be exchanged in any formula of the type $X\,e\,Y$." Once such a rule has been established, it appears that, for example, it is possible to perform the so-called reduction of *Cesare* to *Celarent* purely formally. *Celarent* has the form

(1) *M e P* (major premise)

(2) *S a M* (minor premise)

_____

(3) *S e P* (conclusion).

We can apply our rule directly to (1), and this gives

$$P\ e\ M$$
$$S\ a\ M$$
_____
$$S\ e\ P$$

in other words, *Cesare*.

It may of course be asked whether the application of this method to such simple questions is appropriate. But our example shows that calculation – in the formalistic sense – is applicable outside mathematics, that it *can* be made use of in other fields.

Eidetic and Operational Meaning

From our considerations it appears that a sign can have a twofold meaning, a so-called eidetic and a so-called operational meaning. A sign has an eidetic meaning in a system if we know its semantic counterpart, that is, if we know what it refers to, or what it means. A sign has a purely operational meaning, on the other hand, if we know only how it can be used, that is, if we know only the syntactic rules which are applicable to it. In that case we do not know what the sign *means*, but we do know how we can operate with it. The relationship between the two senses is simple: if an eidetic meaning is given, then an operational meaning is always given along with it, but not the other way round: as we have already seen, it is possible to attach an operational meaning to a sign without also attaching to it an eidetic meaning.

To prevent misunderstandings, it should be stressed that the operation we are discussing here is an operation with signs, a calculation, and not an operation with things. Knowing the operational meaning of signs does not involve knowing at all how the corresponding things are to be treated, since for this we should have to know the eidetic meaning of the signs. For example, it would not be correct to say that the formulas of contemporary theories of the structure of matter have only an operational meaning because they tell us only how to make atom bombs etc. In order to produce an atom bomb we must understand the eidetic meaning of the signs which occur in the formulas. If they had only an operational meaning, we should not be in a position to do anything with them except calculate.

There are two extreme positions in philosophy today: on the one hand it is held that human knowledge is limited to eidetic meanings, and on the other that it is limited to the purely operational. In the first case all formalism is excluded, or at any rate systems which cannot be fully interpreted are rejected. On the other side, it is maintained that there is no such thing as eidetic meaning, and that only operational meaning is at our disposal. Both views are erroneous. It is perfectly clear that in certain cases there is an eidetic meaning. On the other hand, however, there seem to be parts of mathematics, physics, astronomy, etc. which cannot be given any eidetic meaning, although on the whole they lead to consequences which it is possible to interpret eidetically.

Models

This is related to a matter that has been much discussed in recent decades, the problem of models. It is usually said that, whereas earlier physical theories had a model, there is no such model for many modern theories. By "model" is understood a physical structure observable in principle by the naked eye, and having the same form as the state of affairs represented by the scientific statements or theories in question. There is, for example, a model for Bohr's atomic theory: it consists of a ball around which smaller balls revolve at certain distances. Admittedly it is not always possible to construct this kind of model, but it can at least be imagined or represented. If it is said that there is no model for modern physical theories, this means that it is impossible to imagine any such structure for them.

This, however, leads – at any rate in the majority of cases – to the assertion that the scientific statement (theory etc.) in question has no eidetic meaning but only an operational one. We say "at any rate in the majority of cases" since in principle a third, intermediate, case is conceivable in which the statement in question has an eidetic meaning, but one which only corresponds to an intellectually observable structure, not to one that can be represented sensibly or pictorially. There can be no doubt that certain statements of phenomenology, and all the statements of ontology, are of this kind: they have not only an operational but also an eidetic meaning, although it is impossible to represent their meaning pictorially. But with respect to scientific theories having no model, then it holds in most cases that they have no eidetic meaning at all.

In any science the transition from theories with models to theories without usually signifies an extended application of formalism. This is recognised to be the case in many spheres of modern research.

The Nature of Formalism

Formalism is thus a method which consists in completely disregarding the eidetic meaning of signs and operating with them on the basis of certain transformation-rules concerned only with the written shape of the signs. They are treated as though they were not signs but pieces in a game, which can be combined and transposed in various ways. It has therefore been said in jest that anyone who makes use of formalism does not know what he is saying, nor whether what he is saying is true. On this point the following comments must be made.

(1) The goal of calculation, that is of formalism, is always knowledge. A formalistic system only fulfils its task, therefore, if it is ultimately possible to interpret its results eidetically. Science is not a game. But our knowledge does not always attain the *what*; sometimes it is limited to the *how*.

(2) The rules governing formalistic operations must make sense eidetically. For the rules prescribe what we are to do; we must therefore be capable of *understanding* them. It follows that it is impossible to formalize any system completely, or at least that its rules can never be ultimately formalized. It is true that the rules of a system, let us say of system *A*, can be formalized in another system *B*, but system *B* in its turn demands meaningful rules. These can, it is true, again be formalized in a third system *C*, but we have to stop somewhere and use non-formalized rules. Moreover the rules of *A* must already have an eidetic meaning for us while *A* is being built up, since otherwise we could make no progress with our calculation.

(3) In practice, formalized systems are nearly always developed by first establishing meaningful signs, then abstracting from their meaning and building up the system formalistically, and finally giving a new interpretation to the finished system.

(4) The above holds in particular for logic. Although it would not be

impossible to have a science whose system had no meaning except a syntactic one, this cannot be the case with logic. For logic has to provide rules of deduction for all indirect thinking, and if its rules were not eidetically meaningful no deduction could be carried out. Accordingly most contemporary logicians hold that systems which do not permit any known eidetic interpretation are not really logic.

The Justification of Formalism

The following reasons can be advanced for the use of the formalistic method:

(1) In a complicated situation our eidetic understanding of the object very soon breaks down. We can see immediately and without any difficulty that $2 \times 3 = 6$, but only a few people find it just as easy to see that $1952 \times 78,788 = 153,794,176$. We can also see immediately that the negation of "it is raining" is the statement "it is not raining", but it is not so easy to see the negation of the well-known proposition of Euclid that through a point which lies outside a straight line one and only one straight line can be drawn parallel to the given line. The same applies to all somewhat more complicated trains of thought, including those of the philosophers. Their genius has prevented great philosophers from making mistakes without the use of formalism, but the confusions which are in general only too frequent in the field of philosophy derive at least in part from a lack of adequate formalistic methods.

(2) Since in a formalistic system all the rules refer exclusively to the written shape of the signs, it is impossible to construct a proof with unformulated rules and axioms. Unformulated presuppositions, again, are notoriously dangerous; they can easily be false, and since they are not explicitly formulated it is impossible to test them by rational means. The use of formalism therefore makes an important contribution towards the exclusion of such tacit presuppositions.

(3) Something still further is achieved in this way. In an axiomatic system that has been developed formalistically it is possible to derive all the deductive consequences of the chosen axioms fairly easily and definitely. In this process it very often happens that the concepts used are much more exactly defined than was supposed before the beginning of the process. Formalism is therefore well qualified to delimit and clarify concepts and ideas.

(4) Finally the use of formalism leads to the following possibility. If a system is developed purely formalistically, it often turns out in the end to allow of several interpretations, so that at one blow several problems are solved. An example is the well-known duality principle of Euclidean geometry. From the statement: "Any two points determine one straight line" it is possible to derive (with the aid of further axioms and the appropriate rules) a mass of further geometric propositions. We can formalize this statement thus: "Any two A's determine one B"; the meaning of "A" and "B" may remain indeterminate (all the other words that occur in the sentence can be interpreted as merely logical constants.) But it now appears that there are *two* possible interpretations here: (1) One can give to "A" the meaning of "point" and to "B" the meaning of "straight line", (2) or vice versa to "A" the meaning of "straight line" and to "B" the meaning of "point". It appears that the statement arising from interpretation (2) is also true: two parallel straight lines determine a point at an infinite distance. This results, however, in a whole system of statements which can be derived from this (formalized) statement, and we have obtained from one formula *two* principles of geometry. Similar cases may be found in other scientific fields.

We have now given the most important reasons for the use of formalism. But certain associated dangers must not be overlooked. Above all, formalizing must not be undertaken too hastily, before the state of affairs has been suitably clarified. Further it must be borne in mind that a formalistic system is always very abstract and that it must not be equated with reality. Formalism should therefore never be used as the sole method, but rather in conjunction with other methods.

Artificial Languages

The use of an artificial language must be sharply distinguished from formalism. A "natural" (everyday) language could in principle be formalized, and on the other hand an artificial language need not be regarded formalistically; for example, the elementary parts of the language of mathematical logic are usually not so regarded.

The use of artificial symbols did, however, come up at the same time as formalism. Whitehead and Russell justify their use in the following ways.

(1) In the sciences in general, but especially in logic, concepts are

required which are so abstract that it is impossible to find suitable words for them in ordinary language. One is therefore forced to make new symbols.

(2) The syntax of ordinary language is not exact enough, its rules allow for too many exceptions, to make it a good instrument in the field of exact science. It might be possible to overcome the difficulty by retaining the words of ordinary language and only changing the rules, but then by association the words would always be suggesting the loose rules of everyday language, and confusion would ensue. It is therefore better to establish an artificial language with strictly syntactic rules of its own.

(3) If one decides to use an artificial language one can choose quite short symbols, such as single letters instead of whole words; in this way the sentences will be considerably shorter than in ordinary language and substantially easier to understand.

(4) Finally, most of the words used in ordinary language are very ambiguous; thus, for example, the word "is" has at least a dozen distinct meanings which must be kept clearly apart in analysis. It is therefore convenient to use artificial but unambiguous symbols instead of such words. It should be noted that the expression "symbolic language" is misleading: *every* language consists of symbols and could therefore be called "symbolic". What is meant here, however, is a language which, unlike ordinary language, consists of *artificial* symbols.

8. RULES OF SYNTACTIC MEANING

The Construction of Language

From the syntactic point of view a language consists of a mass of expressions to which fixed rules are applicable. In what follows, for simplicity's sake, we shall understand by language a written language; but the treatment would also, with certain limitations, cover a spoken language. The rules of a particular language, let us say of S, determine which expressions belong to S, that is, are meaningful in S; all other expressions are *syntactically meaningless* in this language. Thus, the word "*homme*", for example, while certainly an expression, is meaningless in English.

The meaningful expressions of the language S may be divided into two classes: (1) *Atomic* or simple expressions. These expressions are so constituted that no individual part of them, taken by itself, can be a

43

proper (meaningful) expression of S. Thus, for example, the expression "man" is an atomic expression in English. (2) *Molecular* or compound expressions. In this case individual parts of the expression are already meaningful expressions in S. An example from English: "Man is an organism". Here "man", "organism", and "is", taken by themselves, are already meaningful (atomic) expressions in English.

This division into atomic and molecular expressions is, however, not entirely perfect in the case of natural languages. For example the word "hand" is clearly an atomic expression in English, and yet a part of "hand", namely "and", is also a similar atomic expression. It is true that inconsistencies of this sort could be removed by semantic means, but it is easier and more practical to construct an artificial language in which they do not occur at all.

In this section we are concerned only with the syntactic rules of *molecular* expressions, since only these can be discussed in the absence of the theory of axiomatic systems. We shall deal with the corresponding rules for atomic expressions in the section on axiomatics.

The Idea of a Syntactic Category

With respect to the syntactic significance of the molecular expressions of a language two fundamental rules hold: (1) The molecular expressions must be constructed exclusively out of expressions which are meaningful in the language in question, and therefore in the end only out of meaningful atomic expressions of this language. (2) The construction itself must be done according to the fixed *formation-rules* of the language. The formation-rules of all languages, however, have a common nucleus which may be summed up in the laws of the so-called syntactic categories. We shall therefore first discuss these important syntactic laws.

A class of expressions of a language, each of which can be exchanged with any other of the same class in a meaningful statement without depriving the statement of meaning, is called a *"syntactic category"*. Thus, for example, the proper names constitute a syntactic category of English; in any meaningful English statement – e.g. "Fritz drinks" – one proper name can be replaced by another, without depriving the statement of meaning. In the example quoted "Fritz" can be replaced by "John", "Eva", "Napoleon", or even "Everest", and the statement will still be meaningful (perhaps true, perhaps false, but still meaningful).

On the other hand, a verb, for example, "sleeps", belongs to a different syntactic category; if we were to put "sleeps" in the place of "Fritz" in our statement, the result would be a nonsensical statement: "sleeps drinks".

As can be seen, the concept of the syntactic category corresponds fairly closely to that of the part of speech in ordinary grammar. The difference lies only in the fact that grammar deals with a living and consequently very imprecise language, and therefore its laws are very loose and imprecise. For scientific purposes, however, the aim must be a *perfect* language, for which exact laws can and must be established. Logical syntax stands in the same relationship to grammatical syntax as geometry would to the measurement of real tree trunks: one provides the ideal theoretical foundation for the other.

It is interesting to note in this connection that the syntactic categories – in keeping with the universal function of language, which strives to be an image of reality – mirror the so-called ontological categories. Thus, for example, the syntactic category of proper names corresponds to the ontological category of substance, and that of the so-called one-place functors that of qualities, etc. The correspondence is, however, not quite complete, since between reality and language stands thought, which creates new categories (of ideal entities).

Functors and Arguments

We shall now sketch a simple system of syntactic categories, starting with the concept of a functor and its argument. An expression which determines another is called its "functor"; the determined expression is the "argument". "Determine" is to be taken here in the widest possible sense. For example, in the statement "it is raining and it is snowing" the "and" is said to determine the partial statements ("it is raining" and "it is snowing"), and so to be their functor, while both of these statements are the arguments of "and". Now in every developed language there are two kinds of expression; one kind can only be arguments, for example individual names or statements, and the other kind only functors, for example verbs. We shall call syntactic categories of the first type "primitive categories" and those of the other type "functor categories".

The number of primitive categories is fairly arbitrary, and for sim-

45

plicity we introduce only two, the categories already mentioned of names and of statements. We may accordingly classify all functors in the following way:

(1) According to the syntactic category of their arguments. Thus we distinguish between (a) name-determining functors (e.g. "sleeps", "loves", "is larger than" etc.) (b) statement-determining functors (e.g. "and", "it is not the case that", "or" etc.); (c) functor-determining functors (e.g. "very" in "the child is very beautiful", where the argument is "beautiful").

(2) According to the syntactic category of the molecular expression which consists of the functor and its arguments. Here we distinguish: (a) name-generating functors (e.g. "a good" in "a good child" because in this case the whole expression is a name); (b) statement-generating functors (e.g. the statement-determining functors already mentioned above; "it rains *and* it snows" is again a statement); (c) functor-generating functors (e.g. "loudly" in "the dog barks loudly" where "loudly" with its argument "barks" is again a functor).

(3) According to the number of arguments. We distinguish between monadic functors (e.g. "sleeps", "runs"), dyadic (e.g. "loves", "is larger than") triadic (e.g. "gives": A gives C to B; in this case A, B and C must be understood as arguments of "gives"), and in general n-adic functors.

It will be seen at once that expressions of the natural languages do not fit into this schema, since they are very often *syntactically ambiguous*. For example, the English expression "is eating" sometimes appears as a monadic functor ("What is Fritz doing? He is eating"), sometimes as a dyadic one ("Fritz is eating sausage"). It is true that this ambiguity contributes to the beauty of language and is valuable poetically; but it detracts seriously from the precision and clarity of language and thus provides yet another reason for the use of artificial languages.

Examples of Syntactic Nonsense

On the basis of the foregoing principles we can establish the following general rule: a molecular expression is syntactically meaningful only when there are associated with every functor occurring in it arguments exactly corresponding to its syntactic category both in number and kind. Anything which fails to satisfy this rule is syntactically meaningless.

Here are a few examples from philosophy. Let us take first the pseudo-statement: "being is identical". We call this a pseudo-statement because it has no syntactic meaning at all, and therefore cannot be a genuine statement. For "is identical" is a dyadic functor and can only be used significantly when exactly two arguments are associated with it, as in the statement "the author of Faust is identical with Goethe". But in our pseudo-statement we only have one argument, namely "being". It is therefore syntactically meaningless.

Another example: a philosopher says "Nothing nothings" ("*das Nichts nichtet*"). Here "Nothing" is the argument of "nothings"; this last expression is obviously a monadic, statement-generating and name-determining functor. But how can it be name-determining in this statement? For what, considered syntactically, is "Nothing"? It is evidently not a name although it seems to be something like one. When we say "there is nothing", we are really trying to say "for every x it is not the case that x is here and now". "Nothing" is therefore an abbreviation for the negation. The negation, however, is not a name, but a functor. What the philosopher means may be right, but what he says must be regarded as syntactic nonsense. It is not a statement and it means nothing.

By appealing to such examples the supporters of the neopositivist school have tried to show up the whole of philosophy as meaningless. They have, however, mistaken syntactic nonsense for something quite different, namely semantic nonsense. With the passage of time it has become clear that they have gone much too far. All the same their attacks have contributed to the general awareness today that a poetic language can be used for the communication of scientific ideas only with great caution, since it can so easily conceal syntactic nonsense. Hence the syntactic analysis of meaning has a far greater significance in philosophy today than was formerly the case.

9. SEMANTIC FUNCTIONS AND TYPES

The two Semantic Functions of the Sign

Let us now turn to semantic questions, that is, to problems concerning the relationships between the sign and that of which it is the sign. First of all – and this was already well known to the scholastics – a distinction must be made between two functions of the sign. The sign can on the one hand *refer to* something, and thus be the vehicle of an objective content. We call this the "objective" function. On the other hand, a sign may *express* something subjective, namely the personal situation of a person or animal giving the sign; we call this second function "subjective".

Usually a sign employed in the context of a normal human language has *both* functions. For example, if an observer says, "This is lead", he *refers* principally to something objective, namely a substance called "lead" which is to be found at certain coordinates of space and time. But at the same time he himself *thinks* what he refers to; the fact that he formulates the statement shows that he has this thought, and thus he expresses a subjective situation by means of the statement. The subjective factors which are expressed by a sign are, however, not only thoughts but usually also feelings, volitions, etc., and these often play such a large part that some methodologists call all subjective factors "emotional" as opposed to "objective" or "scientific".

But though in the normal use of signs the two semantic functions are usually combined, it is possible to think of borderline cases in which a sign either expresses nothing subjective or alternatively has no objective reference. In certain forms of music, at any rate, the latter may well be the case. The signs which make up the language of such music have only subjective, perhaps purely emotional, force. Whether the reverse can also hold for statements of ordinary language it is hard to say. But in scientific works it is fairly easy to point out signs and statements which do not express anything at all but serve only to refer to something.

From the methodological point of view one thing is quite clear: in science, in so far as this deals with objects which can be known and hence spoken of, only the reference, that is the first semantic function, is of any importance. What the scientist himself experiences is quite insignificant. An account of his situation may in certain circumstances provide material for a psychological investigation, but it "proves" nothing, because nothing is meant by it, it has no objective reference.

Speaking the Unspeakable

What happens, however, in the case of something which (either in principle or for human beings like ourselves) cannot be known and hence cannot be spoken of? In this matter contemporary methodologists have differing opinions; they may be divided into three groups.

(1) Bergson and Jaspers are the principal spokesmen for the first group.

They and many other philosophers (most of whom belong to the neo-platonic tradition) are of the opinion that, while the unspeakable cannot be spoken, that is, described and communicated by signs which have an objective reference, it can nevertheless be rendered accessible to some extent with the help of a language lacking objective content. Bergson maintains that true philosophical knowledge of the most important elements of reality (e.g. becoming) can only be achieved through "intuition". The content of this intuition cannot be communicated to another, but by means of certain images it can be presented in such a way that another can experience it also. Hence we find no phenomenological descriptions in the works of Bergson, and no demonstrations, but chiefly images, intended to stimulate the powers of intuition. Jaspers also says that his words "mean nothing". They are only pointers indicating the way to those who wish to encounter the unspeakable in an "existential" experience that cannot be expressed in words. For God, the supremely unspeakable, there remain no further signs, but only "ciphers" whose distinguishing mark is exactly not to have any objective semantic function.

(2) Another group of thinkers represents the precisely opposite standpoint. It has been formulated most sharply by Ludwig Wittgenstein in the sentence: "Whereof one cannot speak, thereof one must be silent". For Wittgenstein and his followers "speak" means "use signs with an objective content". According to these philosophers this is not possible in the case of the unspeakable because by definition it cannot be spoken, and to talk about it in a "musical" fashion may be agreeable, but says *nothing*. One of the greatest dangers in the use of language lies in precisely this, that words, which ostensibly should say something, in reality have only an emotional force and hence say nothing.

(3) Finally there is another group of thinkers who, while they accept Wittgenstein's statement in principle, do not conclude from it that the philosopher is bound to restrict himself to objects which are fully knowable. The main representatives of this group are N. Hartmann with his doctrines of the irrational and the Thomists with their theory of the analogical knowledge of God. Hartmann believes that while there are irrational things which are unknowable to us, and therefore unspeakable, yet these irrationals (which he calls "metaphysical") always have an aspect which can be known. Not only can the irrational be delimited, but it can also be dealt with by formulating the antinomies which always

appear in connection with it. According to the Thomist theory of analogy we can, in spite of the fact that the nature of God is beyond our knowledge, nevertheless transfer certain predicates to him by 'analogy'. It is true that we do not and cannot know, for example, what God's thought is, but we can say that it has certain relationships to its object that are proportionately similar to those which hold between human thought and its object. This theory has been extended to the idea that relationships conceived in God are isomorphic with those we know empirically. It is clear that the work of Hartmann and the Thomists is not an attempt to speak the unspeakable, but only that part of it which can be spoken of.

Denotation and Meaning

With respect to the objective function of the sign two distinctions must be made, and this requires some terminological comment. Since the Stoics it has been customary to distinguish denotation (*Bezeichnung*) from meaning (*Bedeutung*). The corresponding terminology still fluctuates even today (Frege, for example, uses "*Bedeutung*" precisely in the sense that we ascribe to "*Bezeichnung*") but the principle is generally recognized and has led to important methodological rules. We say, for example, that the name "horse" *denotes* all individual horses, but at the same time also *means* the quality of being a horse, that which every horse is. It is clear that the denotation corresponds to the extension (*extensio*) of the objective concept and the meaning to its intension (*intensio*). In reference to the denotation, therefore, we use the term "extensional" and in reference to the meaning the term "intensional". It should be added that what is denoted by a name is called the "designate" of this name. It is a matter of dispute whether statements and functors also have designates. For Frege the designate of a statement is its truth-value, that is its truth or falsehood.*

* *Translator's note:* This expression in Frege is more often translated "designation", but I have thought it better to render Bocheński's "*Designat*" by "designate" in view of its other uses in this passage. "*Bezeichnung*" might have been translated "designation", but that is not as close as "denotation" to the intended meaning here. The terminology in this section is historically confused in English as well as in German, and fierce philosophical battles still rage about it. I have been as straightforward as possible about equivalents, with an eye to avoiding unnecessary pedantry even at the risk of a loss of nuance. "*Bedeutung*" becomes "meaning" rather than, say, "significance", even though its contrast with "*Sinn*" in later uses (which has to be translated "meaning" because of "*Sinnlos*", etc.) is thereby sacrificed.

Denotation is an essentially *weaker* function than meaning, in as much as the denotation is always given by the meaning, but not vice versa. The reason is that the same class of designates can be characterized in different ways, and therefore different meanings can correspond to one and the same class of designates. Consider for example the term "triangle". The denotation of the term is given by the enumeration of all triangles; but quite different meanings can correspond to this denotation, based for example on the following characterizations: plane figure with three angles, plane figure with three sides, figure whose internal angles sum to 180°, etc. Each of these characterizations clearly determines the class of designates of the term "triangle".

Nevertheless logic and the natural sciences have a striking tendency to extensional thinking, i.e. to the use of names with regard only to their denotation. This tendency, which in itself might seem odd (and which, incidentally, is opposed by many philosophers and humanists) is understandable because denotation is much easier to handle than meaning. It is true that it does not seem possible ever to exclude meaning completely, since ultimately it is only through the meaning that the denotation can be fixed, but the advantages of the extensional procedure are so great in the fields referred to that it has been made a general rule to proceed extensionally wherever possible.

Semantic Types

In the light of the preceding remarks another important theory of semantics will be more intelligible: the theory of so-called semantic types. The basic idea is that a distinction must be made between language which is about things and language which is about language; the latter is called the "metalanguage" of the former. The theory may be explained more precisely as follows. First of all we take all objects which (from our standpoint) are not signs, as constituting "type 0". Then follows a class of signs which denote these objects, the elements of type 0; we call this class of signs "type 1" or the "object language". To this second class is added a third: it consists of signs which denote the signs of the object language; it forms "type 2" and is the metalanguage of the first language. This procedure can be repeated indefinitely. In general type n is a language which is of such a kind that at least one of its signs denotes a sign of type $n-1$, but none denotes an element of type n itself or of a higher type.

This theory leads to the establishment of a new and important semantic rule: every expression which refers to itself is meaningless. The correctness of this rule can be easily seen on the basis of what has been said; such an expression would belong simultaneously to two semantic types, the object language and the metalanguage at the same time, and this is incompatible with the theory of types.

An example of the application of this rule is the famous "Liar", which troubled all logicians from the time of Plato to the beginning of this century. The sentence is: "What I am saying now is false". This leads directly to a contradiction, since if the speaker is telling the truth then what he says is false, and if he is not telling the truth then what he says is true. The difficulty is easily resolved on the basis of our rule. This shows that the "Liar" is not a statement at all but a piece of semantic nonsense: it is a pseudo-statement in which reference is made to itself.

The "Liar" is only one example of the many *semantic antinomies*. These cannot be solved by syntax alone. It has also come to be realized that many important concepts, for example the concept of truth, the concept of the designate, etc., can be dealt with satisfactorily only on the basis of the metalanguage.

It follows from the foregoing remarks that everything that is to be said *about* a science is to be said not in the language of this science but in its metalanguage, which is also called "meta-science", for example the analysis of a particular scientific symbolism, methodology, and the like. Today a number of sciences have their own meta-science, there being among others a fully developed meta-logic and meta-mathematics.

On the Use of Quotation Marks

In the course of applying the theory of semantic types certain technical rules have been set up for the use of quotation marks. They are now strictly adhered to by most logicians and methodologists of science.

An expression is enclosed between quotation marks when it denotes itself or an expression of the same form: without quotation marks it denotes not itself but something else. In other words: an expression between quotation marks is a sign of the expression itself, and thus a metalinguistic expression in relation to a similar expression without quotation marks.

A few examples will illustrate the significance of this rule. If we write the statement:

a cat is an animal

without putting the second word in quotation marks, then the statement is true, since the second word denotes the familiar domestic animal. But if we write:

a 'cat' is an animal

then we have formulated a false statement, since the word between quotation marks does not denote a cat but the *word* 'cat', and a word is not an animal.

On the other hand the statement:

a 'cat' consists of three letters

is obviously true, but the statement:

a cat consists of three letters

is just as obviously false, since the animal in question certainly does not consist of letters.

An expression between quotation marks is always a *name*, even when without quotation marks it would be a statement or a functor; in quotation marks it is the *name* of this statement or this functor.

Of course quotation marks, in ordinary language, have other uses besides this; for example they are placed round expressions which are not being used in their normal sense. It would, however, be advisable in such cases to choose signs (a different kind of quotation mark) other than those whose technical use has been described here.

10. SEMANTIC MEANING AND VERIFIABILITY

The Methodological Significance of the Problem

As has already been said, a distinction must be made between the syntactic and the semantic meaning of an expression. It can very easily happen that an expression is correctly formed according to the syntactic rules of the language in question, so that it is syntactically meaningful, and that at the same time it has no semantic meaning. In order for a sign to have a semantic meaning, certain *extra-linguistic* conditions must be fulfilled. These conditions are bound up with the verifiability of statements, i.e. with a method which allows us to establish whether a statement is true or false.

Verifiability has acquired great importance for methodological thought through recent developments in the sciences. This is attested to by the following facts:

(1) The progress of modern science first became possible when certain philosophical expressions, namely those whose occurrence in a statement makes it impossible to verify this statement by empirical means, were ruled out.

(2) In the course of the development of science certain scientific expressions were introduced (e.g. "ether") which, like the philosophical expressions mentioned above, proved to be useless.

These circumstances have led to a demand for the exclusion of all such expressions from scientific language. The methodologists of the Vienna Circle, which was founded on positivist philosophy, and the followers of logical empiricism, extended this principle to the whole of knowledge, at first, it is true, in very narrow dogmatic terms. Gradually, however, a more tolerant attitude emerged. For present-day purposes the controversy has resulted in some important and generally valid insights and certain rules of scientific method, but it has also posed a number of difficult problems.

The Verifiability Thesis

There are two fundamental rules, both of which are called the "verifiability thesis". They are:

(1) A statement is semantically meaningful if a method can be demonstrated by which it is verifiable.

(2) An expression which is not a statement is semantically meaningful if it can be incorporated into a semantically meaningful, i.e. verifiable, statement.

These two propositions contain a number of terms which must be understood exactly if the meaning of the rule is to be grasped.

First it should be noted that they do not identify meaning and verifiability. It is true that some philosophers have done this, but their thesis turns out to be untenable: meaning is *not* the same as verifiability; although a statement, *in order* to have meaning, must be verifiable, meaning and verifiability are nevertheless not the same thing.

Further it should be noted that in the propositions given above verifiability is not exactly defined. In this respect also an extreme position was originally adopted, which admitted only one kind of verifiability, based on physical observation of the state of affairs referred to by the statement. A more tolerant attitude prevails today, so that a variety of types of observation is acceptable. According to the view now held the foregoing rules demand only that there shall be *some* method or other by means of which it can be ascertained whether a statement is (to some extent) correct or incorrect.

In order to understand this, consider the following statement: "the window in my room is shut". How could this statement have a meaning if there were no known method of ascertaining the truth of what it asserted? But in fact there is a method, since the speaker knows that if he tried to put his hand through the window it would meet with resistance, etc.

It is worth remarking also that the first proposition enunciated above incorporates, up to a point, all other conditions of meaning. In order to be verifiable a statement must, for example, be syntactically meaningful. It is impossible to verify syntactic nonsense.

What does "Verifiable" Mean?

The meaning of "verifiable" and of "verifiability" is beset with serious difficulties. A statement is verifiable if it can be verified or falsified, that is, if it is *possible* to show that it is true or false. But what does "possible" mean? Reichenbach distinguishes between the following meanings of the term:

(1) *Technical possibility*. This holds when we actually have the means of verifying the statement in question. In this sense, for example, the statement "the temperature at the centre of the sun is 20,000,000 °C" is not directly verifiable. It has, as we shall put it, no technical verifiability.

(2) *Physical possibility*. This holds when the verification of the statement does not violate the laws of nature. The statement given above about the temperature at the centre of the sun is physically verifiable although we have no technical possibility of verifying it. On the other hand, the statement "if a body moves at a speed of 350,000 km/sec, its mass will become vanishingly small" is not physically verifiable, since, according to the laws of physics, no body can move at this speed.

(3) *Logical possibility*. This holds if the verification does not involve a contradiction. The statement given above under (2), even though it is not physically verifiable, is logically verifiable because it contains no contradiction.

(4) *Super-empirical possibility*. As an example of this Reichenbach chooses the statement of a follower of a certain religious sect: "The cat is a divine animal".

This classification of possibilities derives from a positivistic standpoint, and the fourth type of possibility seems to be an illogical concession.* A different classification could be given, according to the types of experience through which a statement might be verifiable. This would yield physical, introspective, phenomenological and supernatural verifiability. There seems to be no doubt, for example, that phenomenologists verify their statements by a special kind of experience, the observation of essences. Similarly religious beliefs, although not verified, are nevertheless verifiable, to be sure not by natural means.

Carnap, for his part, has enunciated the *tolerance principle:* everyone is free to decide what kind of verifiability he intends to allow. But in the sciences today the rule generally holds that statements are to be regarded as meaningful only if they are ultimately verifiable by sense experience. By verifiability, however, is usually understood something somewhat broader than the technical and somewhat narrower than the purely physical.

The Principle of Intersubjectivity

An even stronger form of the verifiability thesis follows from the so-called principle of intersubjectivity. According to this principle, any non-trivial verification must be *intersubjective*, i.e. accessible to several investigators. It is not enough for there to be a method of verification; at least in principle it must be possible for the use of this method to be intersubjective. The neo-positivist methodologists, who first introduced

* *Translator's note:* This is not quite fair to Reichenbach. In the passage referred to he is arguing from types of possibility to types of verifiability and hence to types of meaning, and he does not introduce the super-empirical until the last of these three stages. At this point it is not an illogical concession; the hypothetical cat-worshipper insists on the meaningfulness (not the possibility) of the divinity of cats, and Reichenbach shows that while the claim cannot be disallowed it need not be allowed either – this kind of meaning can always be reduced to one of the other kinds.

this principle, rejected all introspective psychology as meaningless. They believed, that is, that a statement about one's own mental condition could never be verified by anyone else and must therefore be entirely meaningless. And in fact an intersubjective verification does seem to be logically impossible in this case. The principle of intersubjectivity therefore led at first to a thoroughgoing *physicalism*, i.e. to the prohibition of the use of expressions which did not denote physical things or processes.

But it is immediately clear that the strong form of the principle of intersubjectivity would prohibit *every* statement. For even in the physical sphere it is impossible for two investigators to observe *the same* phenomenon: either they will see it one after the other, in which case the interval will have brought about a change in the phenomenon, or they will see it from two different points of view, in which case each will see a different aspect of the phenomenon. *No* verification can be strongly intersubjective.

This principle, while not exactly condemned, tends now to be regarded only as regulative. According to the contemporary view one should as far as possible make use only of such expressions, and formulate only such statements, as are relatively easy for others to verify. When formulated in this way the rule holds good for all domains of knowledge and should be rigidly applied. Unfortunately too many people have not yet realized how important this is. In the empirical sciences – with the exception of psychology, if it is to be regarded as a science – the principle holds in the sense that individual statements should be verifiable by *sense* observation.

Verifiability of Generalizations

But how does this work, it will properly be asked, in the case of general statements? Obviously such a statement can never be verified by sense observation. One could, for example, verify that some phenomenon occurred in 100 cases, or in 100,000, or in 100,000,000, but it is logically impossible to verify that it will occur in *every* possible case. Insofar as one insists on sense verification, generalizations seem to be meaningless. But on the other hand it is impossible to have a science without generalizations, in fact any science consists mainly of such statements and without them could hardly be a science.

57

Now methodologists distinguish between two kinds of generalizations: so-called logical and so-called empirical generalizations. It is usually maintained that the first cannot be verified by observation, and that they do not need to be in order to be meaningful. How such a statement can nevertheless be meaningful is a question on which there are divergent opinions corresponding to various philosophical presuppositions. Philosophers with a phenomenological bias assume that the axioms of logic are verifiable by an intellectual insight, such as an observation of essence; empiricists, on the other hand, regard such statements as *empty*, not it is true as exactly meaningless but as independent of the general rules of semantic meaningfulness. However it may be explained, the fact remains that these logical statements cannot be verified empirically. This constitutes a fundamental difference between contemporary methodology and the earlier views of Comte and Mill.

So-called empirical generalizations, on the other hand, are, according to the most prevalent view, semantically significant if at least one statement can be derived from them which is verifiable by sense observation. Accordingly, for example, the statement "all pieces of sulphur burn with a blue flame" is meaningful since it is possible to derive from it the physically verifiable statement "this piece of sulphur burns with a blue flame". On the other hand the philosophical statement "all pieces of sulphur consist of matter and form" is regarded as meaningless, because it is impossible to derive a physically observable statement from it.

In recent years, however, it has become clear that the precise formulation of this postulate is beset with very serious difficulties. The chief difficulty can be expressed as follows: it is generally not possible to derive anything at all from a single statement, but only from a number of them, for example, from a previously constructed theory. The principle must therefore be extended in this direction. But it turns out that in practice some physically verifiable statement is derivable from *every* statement. Take, for example, the metaphysical statement "the Absolute is perfect". If we conjoin this with the statement "this tree is in bloom" then the statement "there are flowers on this tree" is derivable from the conjunction, and in this way our non-scientific statement about the Absolute becomes scientifically verifiable and significant.

The only solution of this difficulty which now seems feasible is to construct an inventory of scientifically permissible expressions. What is ultimately at issue, of course, is not a truth capable of demonstration but merely a practical rule. Its justification lies in its usefulness for the development of science. In other fields, of course, this question does not arise; only on the basis of highly dubious philosophical dogmas could the usefulness or necessity of such an inventory be defended there.

Another difficulty is posed by terms which denote dispositions, e.g. "soluble". One can verify physically that a substance does in fact dissolve (e.g. in water) but inconsistencies arise when one tries to derive a definition of solubility in water from this. It would be easy to show on the basis of such a definition that every object, e.g. a piece of iron, which is never put in water, must be regarded as soluble in water. Nevertheless science cannot get along without such terms. Carnap has partly solved this difficulty by means of his "reduction sentences".* We cannot go further into these questions here, but they are mentioned in order to draw attention to the important problems posed by the strong form of the principle of verification.

11. Example of Semantic Methods in Practice

Tarski: The Concept of True Sentence in Everyday or Colloquial Language **

For the purpose of introducing the reader to our subject, a consideration – if only a fleeting one – of the problem of defining truth in colloquial language seems desirable. I wish especially to emphasize the various difficulties which the attempts to solve this problem have encountered.

Amongst the manifold efforts which the construction of a correct

---

* *Translator's note:* It seems worth while to give the standard example here. "x is soluble in water" is defined as equivalent to "if x is placed in water then x dissolves". The logical form of this conditional makes it true whenever its antecedent ("x is placed in water") is false; hence if x is not placed in water it is by definition soluble, whatever it may be. The reduction sentence for this case (a *bilateral* one, in Carnap's terminology) reads: "if x is placed in water then x is soluble if and only if x dissolves", thus circumventing the difficulty.

** From: Alfred Tarski, *Der Wahrheitsbegriff in den formalisierten Sprachen.* In: Studia Philosophica, 1, Leopoli 1935, 267–279 (with omissions). I am indebted to Professor Tarski for his kind permission to reprint this text here. (*Translator's note:* The translation of this passage is by J. H. Woodger, from Alfred Tarski, tr. Woodger, *Logic, Semantics, Metamathematics,* Oxford 1956, 154–165 (with omissions). In my turn I am indebted to Professor Woodger, Professor Tarski, and the Delegates of the Clarendon Press, for their kind permission to reprint the translation.)

definition of truth for sentences of colloquial language has called forth, perhaps the most natural is the search for a semantical definition. By this I mean a definition which we can express in the following words:

(1) *a true sentence is one which says that the state of affairs is so and so, and the state of affairs indeed is so and so.*

From the point of view of formal correctness, clarity, and freedom from ambiguity of the expressions occurring in it, the above formulation obviously leaves much to be desired. Nevertheless its intuitive meaning and general intention seem to be quite clear and intelligible. To make this intention more definite, and to give it a correct form, is precisely the task of a semantical definition.

As a starting-point certain sentences of a special kind present themselves which could serve as partial definitions of the truth of a sentence or more correctly as explanations of various concrete turns of speech of the type '*x* is a true sentence'. The general scheme of this kind of sentence can be depicted in the following way:

(2) *x is a true sentence if and only if p.*

In order to obtain concrete definitions we substitute in the place of the symbol '*p*' in this scheme any sentence, and in the place of '*x*' any individual name of this sentence.

If we are given a name for a sentence, we can construct an explanation of type (2) for it, provided only that we are able to write down the sentence denoted by this name. The most important and common names for which the above condition is satisfied are the so-called *quotation-mark names*. We denote by this term every name of a sentence (or of any other, even meaningless, expression) which consists of quotation marks, left- and right-hand, and the expression which lies between them, and which (expression) is the object denoted by the name in question. As an example of such a name of a sentence the name "it is snowing" will serve. In this case the corresponding explanation of type (2) is as follows:

(3) *'it is snowing' is a true sentence if and only if it is snowing.*

Another category of names of sentences for which we can construct analogous explanations is provided by the so-called *structural-descriptive names*. We shall apply this term to names which describe the words which compose the expression denoted by the name, as well as the signs of which each single word is composed and the order in which these signs and words follow one another. Such names can be formulated without the help of quotation marks. For this purpose we must have, in the language we are using (in this case colloquial language), individual names of some sort, but not quotation-mark names, for all letters and all other signs of which the words and expressions of the language are composed. For example we could use '*A*', '*E*', '*Ef*', '*Jay*', '*Pe*' as names of the letters '*a*', '*e*', '*f*', '*j*', '*p*'. It is clear that we can correlate a structural-descriptive name with every quotation-mark name, one which is free from quotation marks and possesses the same extension (i.e. denotes the same expression) and vice versa. For example, corresponding to the name "'snow'" we have the name 'a word which consists of the four letters: *Es, En, O, Double-U* following one another'. It is thus clear that we can construct partial definitions of the type (2) for structural-descriptive names of sentences. This is illustrated by the following example:

(4) *an expression consisting of three words of which the first is composed of the two letters I and Te (in that order) the second of the two letters I and Es (in that order) and the third of the seven letters Es, En, O, Double-U, I, En, and Ge, (in that order), is a true sentence if and only if it is snowing.*

Sentences which are analogous to (3) and (4) seem to be clear and completely in accordance with the meaning of the word 'true' which was expressed in the formulation (1). In regard to the clarity of their content and the correctness of their form they arouse, in general, no doubt (assuming of course that no such doubts are involved in the sentences which we substitute for the symbol '*p*' in (2)).

But a certain reservation is nonetheless necessary here. Situations are known in which assertions of just this type, in combination with certain other not less intuitively clear premises, lead to obvious contradictions, for example the *antinomy of the liar*. We shall give an extremely simple formulation of this antinomy which is due to J. Łukasiewicz.

For the sake of greater perspicuity we shall use the symbol '*c*' as a typographical abbreviation of the expression 'the sentence printed on the bottom line of this page'. Consider now the following sentence:

c is not a true sentence.

Having regard to the meaning of the symbol '*c*', we can establish empirically:

(α) '*c is not a true sentence*' *is identical with c.*

For the quotation-mark name of the sentence *c* (or for any other of its names) we set up an explanation of type (2):

(β) '*c is not a true sentence*' *is a true sentence if and only if c is not a true sentence.*

The premises (α) and (β) together at once give a contradiction:

c is a true sentence if and only if c is not a true sentence.

The source of this contradiction is easily revealed: in order to construct the assertion (β) we have substituted for the symbol '*p*' in the scheme (2) an expression which itself contains the term 'true sentence' (whence the assertion so obtained – in contrast to (3) or (4) – can no longer serve as a partial definition of truth). Nevertheless no rational ground can be given why such substitutions should be forbidden in principle.

I shall restrict myself here to the formulation of the above antinomy and will postpone drawing the necessary consequences of this fact till later. Leaving this difficulty on one side I shall next try to construct a definition of true sentence by generalizing explanations of type (3). At first sight this task may seem quite easy – especially for anyone who has to some extent mastered the technique of modern mathematical logic. It might be thought that all we need do is to substitute in (3) any sentential variable (i.e. a symbol for which any sentence can be substituted) in place of the expression 'it is snowing' which occurs there twice, and then to establish that the resulting formula holds for every value of the variable, and thus without further difficulty reach a sentence which includes all assertions of type (3) as special cases:

(5) *for all p, '*p*' is a true sentence if and only if p.*

But the above sentence could not serve as a general definition of the expression '*x* is a true sentence' because the totality of possible substitutions for the symbol '*x*' is here restricted to quotation-mark names. In order to remove this restriction we must have recourse to the well-known fact that to every true sentence (and generally speaking to every sentence) there corresponds a quotation-mark name which denotes just that sentence. With this fact in mind we could try to generalize the formulation (5), for example, in the following way:

(6) *for all x, x is a true sentence if and only if, for a certain p, x is identical with 'p' and p.*

At first sight we should perhaps be inclined to regard (6) as a correct semantical definition of 'true sentence', which realizes in a precise way the intention of the formulation (1) and therefore to accept it as a satisfactory solution of our problem. Nevertheless the matter is not quite so simple. As soon as we begin to analyse the significance of the quotation-mark names which occur in (5) and (6) we encounter a series of difficulties and dangers.

Quotation-mark names may be treated like single words of a language, and thus like syntactically simple expressions. The single constituents of these names – the quotation marks and the expressions standing between them – fulfil the same function as the letters and complexes of successive letters in single words. Hence they can possess no independent meaning. Every quotation-mark name is then a constant individual name of a definite expression (the expression enclosed by the quotation marks) and in fact a name of the same nature as the proper name of a man. For example, the name '*p*' denotes one of the letters of the alphabet. With this interpretation, which seems to be the most natural one and completely in accordance with the customary way of using quotation marks, partial definitions of the type (3) cannot be used for any significant generalizations. In no case can the sentences (5) or (6) be accepted as such a generalization. In applying the rule called the rule of substitution to (5) we are not justified in substituting anything at all for the letter '*p*' which occurs as a component part of a quotation-mark name (just as we are not permitted to substitute anything for the letter '*t*' in the word '*true*'). Consequently we obtain as conclusion not (5) but the following sentence: '*p' is a true sentence if and only if it is snowing.* We see at once from this that the sentences (5) and (6) are not formulations of the thought we wish to express and that they are in fact obviously senseless. Moreover, the sentence (5) leads at once to a contradiction, for we can obtain from it just as easily in addition to the above given consequence, the contradictory consequence: '*p' is a true sentence if and only if it is not snowing.* Sentence (6) alone leads to no contradiction, but the obviously senseless conclusion follows from it that the letter '*p*' is the only true sentence.

The breakdown of all previous attempts leads us to suppose that there is no satisfactory way of solving our problem. Important arguments of a general nature can in fact be invoked in support of this supposition as I shall now briefly indicate.

A characteristic feature of colloquial language (in contrast to various scientific languages) is its universality. It would not be in harmony with the spirit of this language if in some other language a word occurred which could not be translated into it; it could be claimed that 'if we can speak meaningfully about anything at all, we can also speak about it in colloquial language'. If we are to maintain this universality of everyday language in connexion with semantical investigations, we must, to be consistent, admit into the language, in addition to its sentences and other expressions, also the names of these sentences and expressions, and sentences containing these names, as well as such semantic expressions as 'true sentence', 'name', 'denote', etc. But it is presumably just this universality of everyday language which is the primary source of all semantical antinomies, like the antinomies of the liar or of heterological words. These antinomies seem to provide a proof that every language which is universal in the above sense, and for which the normal laws of logic hold, must be inconsistent. This applies especially to the formulation of the antinomy of the liar which I have given on pages 61 and 62, and which contains no quotation-function with variable argument. If we analyse this antinomy in the above formulation we reach the conviction that no consistent language can exist for which the usual laws of logic hold and which at the same time satisfies the following conditions: (I) for any sentence which occurs in the language a definite name of this sentence also belongs to the language; (II) every expression formed from (2) by replacing the symbol 'p' by any sentence of the language and the symbol 'x' by any sentence is to be regarded as a true sentence of this language; (III) in the language in question an empirically established premise having the same meaning as (α) can be formulated and accepted as a true sentence.

If these observations are correct, then *the very possibility of a consistent use of the expression 'true sentence' which is in harmony with the laws of logic and the spirit of everyday language seems to be very questionable, and consequently the same doubt attaches to the possibility of constructing a correct definition of this expression.*

CHAPTER IV

THE AXIOMATIC METHOD

12. GENERAL REMARKS

The Structure of the Indirect Acquisition of Knowledge

If the object of which knowledge is acquired is not given directly it has to be known through some other object, i.e. indirectly. Since the object is a state of affairs, and this itself is expressed in a sentence, every indirect acquisition of knowledge proceeds by inference from one sentence to another or by the *derivation* of the second sentence from the first. It is one of the most important insights of exact methodology that the truth of a sentence must be either apprehended directly or inferred; there is not, and furthermore there cannot be, any other way. In what follows, however, we shall be speaking, as is customary today, not of sentences but of (meaningful) statements.

How does an inference come about? There are two conditions: *first* a statement which is known to be true, *second* a rule which allows us to recognize another statement as true "on the basis" of this statement. On closer examination it appears that the given statement must always be compound; what is needed is a conjunction (a logical product) of at least two statements.* Here is a simple example: we have a conditional statement of the form "if A, then B" and in addition a statement of the form "A"; we also have a rule of inference which may be formulated as follows: "Whenever there occurs in the system a conditional statement ("if A, then B") and also a statement identical with its antecedent ("A"), a statement identical with the consequent of this conditional ("B") may be introduced." On the basis of the statement and with the help of the given rule we infer "B".

This example can be generalized by taking premises of the form

---

* *Translator's note:* This is not strictly true. For example from the simple statement A and the rule of double negation we can infer "it is not the case that not-A".

$F(p_1, p_2, p_3, \ldots, p_n)$ and p_j (where $1 \ll j \ll n$), the rule of inference allowing the conclusion p_k ($1 \ll k \ll n$). It may also happen that instead of p_j or p_k we have their negations – but the basic structure always remains the same. Every indirect acquisition of knowledge has this and no other form.

A few further terminological remarks. The given statements are called "premises"; the derived statement is called a "conclusion"; the operation in which the premises and the rule are explicitly formulated so as to demonstrate the conclusion is called a "proof". The rule of inference given above, which is frequently encountered, is the rule *modus ponendo ponens,* or more briefly, *modus ponens.*

Law and Rule

The foregoing remarks may perhaps not be immediately clear to everyone. Why, it might be asked, do we need rules? Take for example a categorical syllogism in *Barbara:*

> *All logicians smoke pipes*
> *All methodologists are logicians*
> *Therefore all methodologists smoke pipes.*

The conclusion follows, it may be said, directly from the premises, and moreover it requires no conditional statement; it is simply a categorical syllogism.

But that is not the case. It is noteworthy that Aristotle, the founder of categorical syllogistics, hardly ever constructs his syllogisms in the form given above. He would formulate our example as follows:

> *If all logicians smoke pipes*
> *and all methodologists are logicians,*
> *then all methodologists smoke pipes.*

In this case to get a conclusion ("all methodologists smoke pipes"), it is necessary to have another premise, namely the (compound) statement:

> *All logicians smoke pipes,*
> *and all methodologists are logicians.*

Although the syllogism itself is a categorical one, the proof is obtained only by presupposing *modus ponendo ponens.* And this *modus* must be conceived not as a law but as a rule. A law says what *is* – in our case if so-and-so, then so-and-so; but we need to know what we *can do;* and this can be given only by a rule.

Of course it is not necessary to think of this rule in every case of drawing a conclusion; the process is often so simple and natural that we apply it without further ado. But in the first place the situation is not always so simple as in our syllogism; in the higher regions of thought it is hardly ever simple, on the contrary, it is usually all too complex. And in the second place, for the reasons given in the chapter on formalism, we have often to use formalism in such complicated processes of proof. But when we do this, then we abstract from the meaning of the sentences used and cannot proceed at all without an explicitly formulated rule.

These are the grounds on which theorists of the axiomatic method justify their distinction between law and rule.

The Two Basic Forms of Inference

The distinction between laws and rules not only has great theoretical significance, but also makes it possible, as Łukasiewicz has shown, to divide all methods of inference into two principal classes, namely deduction and reduction. We shall use this division as a general framework for the further exposition of modern methods of thought.

The presupposition is that in all proofs the premises can be so transformed that one is a conditional statement ("if A, then B"), and the other is identical either with the antecedent or with the consequent of this statement. Furthermore this is in fact the case: mathematical logic always enables us to effect such a transformation. The two cases can be set out as follows:

> (1) *if A, then B*   (2) *if A, then B*
>   *A*   *B*
>   *therefore B*   *therefore A*

An inference which follows the first pattern Łukasiewicz calls a "deduction", one which follows the second pattern a "reduction". The rule of inference used in deduction is the *modus ponens* already mentioned; this presents no difficulty. On the other hand the rule employed in reduction may seem questionable, since in logic the inference from the consequent to the antecedent of a conditional statement is invalid. And yet the corresponding rule is very often used, in everyday life as well as more especially in the sciences.

Łukasiewicz shows that so-called induction is a special case of reduction. Let us take a simple example: there are three pieces of white phosphorus, *a*, *b*, *c*, for which it has been established that they ignite at 60 °C; we infer from this that *all* pieces of white phosphorus do so. What is the pattern of this process of inference? Obviously it is the following:

If all pieces of white phosphorus ignite at 60 °C, then a, b, and c do; a, b, and c ignite at 60 °C, therefore all pieces of white phosphorus ignite at 60 °C.

This, however, is quite clearly a reduction, since we have inferred the antecedent from a conditional statement and its *consequent*. Such inductions are used in every science, and they are in fact more frequent than any other process of inference (even if they do not have the simple form of the example given here).

Reduction poses very difficult problems, which have not yet been finally solved and which will be dealt with in greater detail in the next section. First of all a little more must be said about types of rules of inference.

Infallible and Fallible Rules of Inference

When we consider the two forms of inference more closely we see that there is a fundamental difference between them: *modus ponens*, which serves as the rule of deduction, is an absolutely infallible rule of inference; on the other hand the corresponding rule of reduction is not infallible.

When is a rule of inference infallible? The answer is when, and only when, if the premises are true, the conclusion derived with the help of this rule is also true. And this holds for all possible premises, in so far as they have the form described above. This is a matter of universal validity, which is sometimes called "a priori", and which obviously pertains to a special field. This field is called logic, or strictly speaking formal logic. It is true that a rule of inference does not belong directly to logic – at least not in the usual sense – but an infallible rule of inference always corresponds to a law which has absolute validity in logic and on the basis of logical principles.

The following comments may be made on the relationship between formal logic and the methodology of the indirect acquisition of knowledge.

(1) A sharp distinction must be made between logic and methodology; logic investigates only universally valid statements, but methodology does not confine itself to them.

(2) Logic forms the direct basis of deductive methodology, in so far as it is possible to translate its laws directly into infallible rules of deductive inference.

(3) Furthermore, logic plays yet another role in every process of inference in that the first premise is very often obtained by substitution into a law of logic. Thus the premise in the example about phosphorus given above has clearly been formed by substitution into the following law of logic:

If for all x, if x is A, x is also B, then if a, b and c are A, they are also B. It follows that there are, not two logics, but two methodologies: the deductive and the reductive. The relation of formal logic to these is asymmetrical: for deduction formal logic supplies not only the first premise but also the basis of the rule of inference; reduction on the other hand requires logic for the formation only of the first premise, not of the rule of inference. But in both cases it is the *same* logic, although one part is made use of here and another there. There is no such thing as inductive or reductive logic, much less a "logic of research" and of "discovery".

Historical Preliminaries

The methodology of the indirect acquisition of knowledge is much older than that of its direct acquisition; it seems even to be older than formal logic, since we already find its beginnings in the pre-Socratics, in Plato and in the early Aristotle, although as yet no genuine logic. In his later years Aristotle developed systematically not only the first logic but also some basic ideas of the methodology of inference, including the idea of an axiomatic system. It appears that in antiquity such systems were developed mainly in mathematics, but we know that the Stoics also axiomatized the rules of logic. For a long time there was no further development; the axiomatics developed by Aristotle as a postulate for all deductive sciences remained in practice the privilege of mathematics. Euclid created the prototype in this field. The scholastics, and more especially the rationalist philosophers of the 18th century, maintained, it is true, the validity of this method for philosophy also. Spinoza, as is well known, wished to construct his ethics *more geometrico*, i.e. axiomatically; but his attempt was a lamentable failure.

In recent times the application of this method has been extended considerably. There are now axiomatized physical theories. Logic itself, since its adoption by mathematics, is usually presented in axiomatized form. At the same time in the twentieth century there have been undertaken the first serious studies of the axiomatic system itself since Aristotle. Husserl reintroduced the distinction (already familiar to the Stoics) between law and rule. The rigorous modern concept of consistency was first formulated by Bolzano and then, independently, by Tarski. To the latter, along with Carnap, we owe the most important insights into the properties of the axiomatic system.

Plan of Exposition

We have to confine ourselves here to what is simplest and most essential in the highly developed field of axiomatic theory. There follow, therefore, a few general remarks about the present state of mathematical logic, after which we shall discuss the basic outlines of axiomatics itself. Since the analysis of the concept is one of the most important results of axiomatization, there will follow a section on scientific concept formation and definition. Finally, a few further points of the axiomatic system will be discussed in detail.

13. THE AXIOMATIC SYSTEM

Preliminary Features of the Axiomatic System

The word "axiom" comes from the Greek ἀξιόω, which indicates a positive evaluation, and in particular an acknowledgement of validity. In Aristotle (but not in the Stoics) "axiom" always means a statement which serves as a "principle" (ἀρχή) from which other statements are derived. Accordingly, an axiomatic system may be roughly characterized as follows: we divide all the statements in some field into two classes: (1) the class of axioms and (2) the class of derived statements; these are deduced from the axioms, and follow from them. Euclid's system of geometry is a classic example of this kind of axiomatic system.

The modern methodology of deduction modifies the older system as follows:

1. The axiomatic system is developed in a purely formal way; it is a system of *signs*. The interpretation of these signs is not part of the system.

2. With formalization all the conditions imposed on the axioms by the old axiomatic system – such as self-evidence, certainty, ontological

priority – become untenable. An axiom differs from the other statements of the system in virtue *only* of the fact that it is not derived in the system.

3. Axioms are sharply distinguished from *rules*. The modern axiomatic system therefore has two kinds of principles: axioms (which are laws) and rules (which are not laws but instructions).

4. By the use of formalism and the distinction between axioms and rules the concept of derivation has been made relative: we no longer speak of derivation or provability in general but always with reference to a given system.

5. In addition to the axiomatic system of statements there is now available a similar and closely associated axiomatic system of terms.

Construction of an Axiomatic System of Statements

In the formation of an axiomatic system the current procedure is as follows:

First a class of statements, which are to function as axioms, is selected; these are inserted into the system without proof. In addition to the axioms, rules of inference are laid down which are to govern all operations in the system. By means of these rules new (derived) statements are then deduced from the axioms. At every step it is precisely specified from which axioms and with the help of which rules the derivation proceeds, and so on step by step. From the derived statements (with or without the use of the axioms) still further statements are derived on the basis of the same rules and in exactly the same way. And this goes on as long as may be necessary.

It is clear, therefore, that an axiomatic system is completely determined by its axioms and rules alone. All the rest is merely an unfolding of what is already given in them.

It is also clear that from the semantic point of view an axiomatic system always contains two kinds of element: the axioms and the derived statements belong to an object-language, the rules to a metalanguage. Only the former can (or should) be formalized, since, if the rules were to be formalized, i.e. abstracted from their meaning, it could not be known what they said, and consequently they could not be used. This means, however, that there is no such thing as a completely formalized axiomatic system. Such a system is nevertheless called "completely formalized" when everything in it, except the rules, is treated formally.

It should be remarked further that in recent years axiomatic systems of a rather different kind have been constructed, for example systems in which there are no axioms, but only rules, and also systems in which other, derived rules are deduced from the basic rules. These systems, however, are of interest only for the methodology of logic, and not for any other field.

Requirements for an Axiomatic System

Not every axiomatic system is now considered to be sound, even if it is strictly formalized and exactly derived. Further conditions are always imposed, which may be divided into two classes. Those of the first class are to be regarded as holding absolutely, those of the second class less strictly.

(1) The axiomatic system is required to be consistent. This postulate was already laid down by Aristotle, but today it is formulated much more severely and is regarded as more absolute. The requirement is not only that no contradiction should be discoverable, but it involves a proof that no contradiction *can* occur in the system. This proof, which can be approached in a number of ways, is required because mathematical logic shows that from a contradiction *every* statement in the field is derivable; this means, however, that there would no longer be* any difference between admissible (true) and inadmissible (false) statements, and this would destroy any science.

(2) To the second group belong the requirements of completeness of the system and of the mutual independence of the axioms. A system is called "complete" if all true statements in its field are derivable from its axioms; the axioms are independent if none of them is derivable from the others. There is a certain aesthetic quality about this postulate. In fact aesthetic reasons seem to play a greater part in axiomatics today than was formerly the case. An effort is being made, for example, to find the smallest possible number of axioms, even a single one, from which all corresponding statements would be derivable, and to make this axiom as simple as possible. This aesthetic tendency goes so far today that often for the sake of simplicity a single less illuminating axiom is preferred to several that are perfectly clear.

---

* *Translator's note:* i.e. if the system did in fact contain a contradiction.

One further requirement has not been mentioned here, although it was touched on before, namely the requirement of strict formalization. This requirement, it is true, is adhered to rigidly only by mathematical logicians; mathematicians usually proceed with much greater freedom, and often with the aid of intuition.

Constructional Systems

A modern axiomatic system includes not only axioms, rules of inference and derived statements but also – and above all – a so-called constructional system *(Konstitutionssystem)* which can be regarded as an axiomatic system of expressions. It is constructed analogously to the axiomatic system of statements, and, like it, has three kinds of components and is developed in the following manner:

First a class of expressions is decided on which are to function as primitives; these are inserted into the system without definition. In addition certain rules are laid down, according to which it is permissible to introduce new atomic expressions into the system (rules of definition) and to form compound expressions (formation-rules). With the aid of these rules new expressions are defined in terms of or formed out of the primitive expressions. At every step it is precisely specified which primitive expressions and rules are being used. From the expressions thus defined (or obtained by combination) new expressions are again introduced (with or without the use of the primitive expressions). And this goes on for as long as may be necessary. The whole process runs exactly parallel to that by which a system of statements is constructed. It is clear that the constructional system is fundamental to the system of statements, since before it can be decided which statements are valid, it must be known which expressions are admissible. But this is determined by the rules of the constructional system. These rules are of three kinds:

1. The rule which determines which expressions are to be taken as primitive.

2. The rules of definition, which determine how new atomic expressions are to be introduced.

3. The formation-rules, according to which further (molecular) expressions are to be formed from the expressions already contained in the system.

The latter rules have already been discussed in the chapter on syntax.

73

The first rule needs no particular discussion; on the other hand, a few remarks may be appropriate on the various kinds of definition. Since these are closely bound up with methodologically important problems of concept formation, we shall discuss them in a special chapter.

Progressive and Regressive Deduction

Viewed from outside, the construction of a formalized axiomatic system always seems to be *progressive*, in that the principles (axioms and rules) are posited first, and the deductions follow from them. In fact, however, not every deduction is progressive, but a distinction has to be drawn between two types of deductive inference: the progressive and the regressive. Both are genuine *deductions*, i.e. the truth of the premises is already known, and it is sought to establish that of the conclusions. But it is possible to proceed independently either from the premises which are already established or from the conclusion which has yet to be proved. Euclid's proofs are an example of regressive deduction: first the statement to be proved is enunciated, and then laws already known, which are necessary for the proof, are adduced. Ordinary calculation, on the other hand, is usually carried out in a progressive form: the final conclusion is formulated only at the end.

If it is asked which of the two kinds of deduction is more frequently used in scientific practice, it turns out that in most cases the conclusions are presented first and then their justification is sought for, i.e. the process is regressive. It is well known, for example, that great mathematical discoveries have very often come about in this way: the discoverer first propounded a thesis, the proof of which was not produced until much later, although from premises long since known.

It does not follow that progressive deduction plays no part in contemporary deductive sciences. On the contrary. Every calculation, as was said above, is obviously a progressive deduction.

One further comment may be added here. Axiomatization itself is completely neutral, not only with respect to the two kinds of deduction, but also with respect to deduction and reduction; it is possible to axiomatize just as well on the basis of axioms already established as on the basis of conclusions already propounded. We refer to this method in the section on deduction only because axiomatization is an abstraction from the actual process of progressive deduction and reflects its structure.

14. MATHEMATICAL LOGIC

Methodological Significance

It cannot be the task of this book to provide an outline of mathematical logic, since this logic is formal, while here we are concerned only with methodology which, as has been emphasized more than once, is to be distinguished from formal logic. However, a brief discussion, if not of a system of mathematical logic at any rate of some of its general features, may be appropriate. Mathematical logic, like every kind of formal logic, can be considered from two points of view. On the one hand it may be regarded as a theoretical discipline, pursuing its own purely theoretical problems. As such it includes, among other things, the search for the single, most economical axiom from which all laws of logic are derivable, or for the sole functor in terms of which all functors of some field of logic may be defined. From this standpoint mathematical logic is a special science which is of no interest to us here.

On the other hand formal logic, as has already been remarked, provides the basis for the rules of deductive inference, and also plays a certain role in the processes of scientific thought. Now its proponents maintain that mathematical logic *is* formal logic, indeed the only scientifically acceptable formal logic. From this point of view a consideration of mathematical logic ought not to be omitted from a study of deductive methodology. Mathematical logic has methodological, as well as purely theoretical and speculative, significance.

In fact, in recent years, mathematical logic has exerted a great influence on methodology, and this for two reasons. In the first place it was the first discipline for which a rigorous axiomatic method was developed, and while this method is also used in many other fields, it is still in mathematical logic that it has the most important role. Moreover, the structure of present-day mathematics (unlike the earlier forms of logic) is such that it poses certain interesting and indeed urgent methodological problems.

This being the case, there are today only a few methodologists of deduction who are not at the same time mathematical logicians, and that is another reason why, in this brief account, we must say something about mathematical logic.

History of Mathematical Logic

In order to understand the contemporary position it may be useful to give a few details of the evolution of mathematical logic. Its history falls into two distinct periods. Leibniz (1646–1716) is generally considered to have been the first mathematical logician, or at any rate the first to have developed certain ideas in mathematical logic. These ideas had no influence on his contemporaries and immediate successors; it was not until about 1900 that they were rediscovered. The history of this discipline really begins with Boole (1815–1864) and de Morgan (1806–1878) who published the first books on the subject in 1847. The works of Couturat (1868–1914) and others also belong to this first period, which can now be regarded as completely superseded. At the end of the 19th century, however, a number of important logicians, notably Frege (1848–1925), and along with him Peano (1858–1932) and Schröder (1841–1902), began to develop a new form of mathematical logic. These beginnings were continued and extended in the great work of Whitehead (1861–1947) and Russell (1872), *Principia Mathematica* (1910–1913). With this work a new period of research commenced.

Basically *Principia Mathematica* represents only a formalistic elaboration and extension of Aristotelian and Stoic formal logic. A characteristic of the third and most recent period, which began about 1920, is the appearance of "heterodox" systems constructed on a different non-Aristotelian and non-Stoic foundation. The most significant of these are the many-valued logic of Łukasiewicz (1921) and the intuitionist logic of Heyting (1930). At the same time there have appeared various Aristotelian systems which differ from the *Principia*, as for example that of Lesniewski (between 1920 and 1935). The most recent development has produced a large number of very original systems, including the so-called natural logics (logics of consequence which consist only of rules) of Gentzen and Jaskowski, and the combinatory logic of Curry (1930).

Essential Features of Mathematical Logic

Numerous misconceptions about mathematical logic have been disseminated by many philosophers of various opinions. The discipline has been identified with the whole of logic (including the methodology and philosophy of logic); it has been identified with a philosophical school, namely neo-positivism (although neither mathematical logic nor its most important founders had anything to do with neo-positivism); it has been said that it is an attempt to reduce everything to quantities, whereas in fact almost the opposite is true (Whitehead and Russell, at least, tried to explain away quantity); and even today it is still confused with some *one* of the many systems of mathematical logic, and even with the philosophical views of certain mathematical logicians. All these misunderstandings are due to superficial knowledge or ignorance of the facts.

Mathematical logic as it exists today is something quite different. It can best be characterized – since it is a kind of formal logic – by distinguishing it from other types of formal logic. It differs from them in that it is *first* axiomatized, *second* formalized, and *third* relativized, in the sense that it comprises many very different systems. A secondary characteristic (which is often mistakenly considered fundamental) is that it is usually expounded in an artificial symbolic language; another similarly accidental but nevertheless important characteristic is that its content is incomparably richer than that of any other type of formal logic. It comprises, for example, the whole of Aristotle's syllogistics in a very precise form, the whole of modal logic, the whole of the Stoic theory of implication, and many thousands more.

Formalism and the axiomatic method having already been dealt with above, there is no need to say anything more about them here, beyond remarking that the axiomatization and formalization of mathematical logic are now taken as paradigmatic and have thus acquired great methodological significance. Anyone who wishes to become acquainted with the axiomatic method must study works on mathematical logic.

Something must still be said about the relativity of systems of mathematical logic, and some of the methods developed in this discipline which are of importance for all deductive thinking must also be discussed briefly.

The Relevance of Mathematical Logic to Non-Logical Axiomatic Systems

If a formalized axiomatic system is to be constructed in any field, for example, in physics, astronomy, biology or theology, the use of mathematical logic is inevitable. This can come about in two ways. (1) The system may be so constructed that all the axioms belong to the discipline in question, i.e. so that it does not incorporate any of the laws of logic.

But if any inferences are to be drawn certain rules of inference must be made use of, and, as practice shows in such cases, fairly many of them. Where is the scientist to get these rules of inference? Obviously from logic. This in fact will supply either ready-made rules of inference (from systems of implication) or, at a minimum, laws which can be directly translated into such rules. (2) But it is also possible – and this is usually the case – to add to the special axioms of the field in question a number of laws borrowed from logic. In this case only a few rules of inference are needed (two or three are often sufficient), although the logical axioms will be correspondingly more numerous.

From this situation, in view of the present position of mathematical logic, an important problem arises. Which among the many systems of this logic is to be used as the basis of axiomatization, whether in the first or second sense? This is an entirely new problem. Earlier methodologists were not aware of it, nor could they be, since the older logic – before 1921 – did not offer alternative systems. But in 1921 (simultaneously and independently of one another) Łukasiewicz and Post set up so-called many-valued systems of logic differing radically from "classical" logic. Łukasiewicz's systems have since been strictly axiomatized, their consistency and completeness proved, etc. There followed the so-called intuitionist logic of Brouwer; in 1930 this too was formulated in strictly axiomatic terms by Heyting. Today there are dozens of alternative systems, and the difference between them is considerable. Thus, for example, the *tertium non datur* (the law of the excluded middle) holds neither in the three-valued logic of Łukasiewicz, nor in Heyting's intuitionist logic, although it is a law of "classical" mathematical logic (such as that for example of *Principia Mathematica*).

The Relativity of Logical Systems

All this might be thought pure speculation on the part of logicians, of no importance for the day-to-day business of science. But that is not the case. In 1944 Reichenbach showed that quantum mechanics cannot be axiomatized without contradiction on the basis of "classical" logic (such as that of *Principia Mathematica*) but that it can be axiomatized straightforwardly without contradiction in the framework of Łukasiewicz's three-valued logic. The assessment of the relative merits of systems of mathematical logic has become a problem for methodology. If demonstrations are to be carried out a logical system must be assumed; but there are now many such systems. Which one should be chosen?

The answer is the one which allows the field to be axiomatized without contradiction in the simplest way. The guiding principle on the one hand is completeness and on the other consistency. In addition, aesthetic considerations also play a part: the simpler and more elegant the proofs in a system, and the fewer the axioms, the better. That is how things stand today, and all serious workers in the methodology of the deductive sciences are in agreement about it.

So much for the methodological content of the new discoveries. Now for a brief philosophical comment. Far too many thinkers have drawn premature philosophical conclusions from this state of affairs in the direction of absolute relativism and scepticism. In fact, however, there seems to be no reason for such pessimistic conclusions. On closer examination the following considerations come to light:

(1) The so-called "heterodox" systems of logic are applied only in fields where signs are unlikely to acquire eidetic meaning. "Classical" logic is used in all sciences which operate with eidetically meaningful signs.

(2) The metalinguistic rules used in the formalization of the systems in question are thoroughly "classical". The three-valued logic of Łukasiewicz, for example, does not admit *tertium non datur*, but on the metalinguistic level it is always taken for granted that each statement has a certain truth-value or does not have it, and that no third alternative is possible. For that matter there are systems in which the principle of contradiction does not hold, but these systems must themselves be constructed without contradictions, and every logician tries to provide a proof of this consistency.

(3) In most cases involving apparently contradictory logical systems either one of them is without an interpretation or the signs used do not have the same meaning in both. Thus, for example, the sign of negation has completely different meanings in intuitionist logic and in the system of *Principia Mathematica*.

(4) On the other hand, such systems often represent only a fraction of the whole domain of logical principles. It may be that such a partial logic is enough for the uses to which it is to be put.

In this way a philosopher who was not sceptically inclined might sum up the methodological situation in this area. And this judgement is appended here because most scientists, after all, are not sceptics. Their intuitive belief in the absolute validity of the laws of logic is not in the least threatened by recent developments. Talk about scepticism comes not from logic itself but from philosophizing methodologists.

Implication and Deducibility

Among the many concepts with which mathematical logic is concerned, the concept of *consequence* plays an especially important role. It is fundamental for the methodology of the indirect acquisition of knowledge since this always presupposes it. Now present-day classical mathematical logic distinguishes at least two concepts of consequence. These are implication and deducibility. Implication is an absolute concept in so far as it can exist between two statements without their having any relationship to an axiomatic system; deducibility, on the other hand, must always be considered in relation to an axiomatic system.

Implication holds between two statements – an antecedent *A* and a consequent *B* – when either *A* is false or *B* is true or both. It follows from this definition that implication fails to hold in one case only, namely when the antecedent (*A*) is true and the consequent (*B*) false; in all other cases, whatever *A* and *B* may be, there is an implication. In particular a false statement implies every statement and a true statement is implied by every statement. Examples (in which the "if–then" is given this interpretation) might be: "If $2 + 2 = 5$, then all dogs are fish"; "if $2 + 2 = 5$, then a healthy dog has 4 feet"; "if $2 + 2 = 4$, then $1 = 1$".

This, as can easily be seen, is a most remarkable interpretation of the usual "if–then", and, what is worse, it leads to methodological difficulties. The Scholastics, and even earlier the Megarians (Diodorus Cronus), tried to avoid these difficulties by defining implication in terms of the (modal) functor of possibility: "If *A*, then *B*" would mean "It is not possible that *A* and not *B*". The same definition was proposed once again by C. I. Lewis in 1918. This, however, fails to remove the difficulties, for if the Diodorian or Lewisian definition is adopted, while the proposition that implication holds between any false statement and any other arbitrary statement is admittedly no longer true, an analogous one is true: it holds between any impossible statement and any other arbitrary statement.

Mathematical logic, however, offers another similar concept, namely that of deducibility. *B* is said to be deducible from *A* in system *S* if and only if S contains axioms and rules such that, if A is in S, B can also be shown to be in S. The following simple example may serve to illustrate the difference between implication and deducibility. Consider the classical syllogism:

(1) All men are mortal
(2) George Boole was a man
(3) George Boole was mortal.

Since (2) and (3) are true, the minor premise (2) implies the conclusion (3). But from (2) alone (3) cannot be deduced on the basis of any ordinary logic. (3) can be deduced only from both the previous statements, i.e. (1) *and* (2). (3) is therefore implied by (2), but it is not deducible from (2) alone.

Obviously it is impossible to deduce anything from a false statement on the strength of its falsity alone; on the other hand a true statement cannot be deduced from any other statement merely because it is true. The concept of deducibility is therefore in some respects closer to the ordinary concept of consequence than is the concept of implication. The concept of consequence has, however, certain properties in common with implication, and it seems also, in the ontological sense, to include causality. Strictly speaking, therefore, implication and deducibility should be kept logically distinct from one another.

15. DEFINITION AND CONCEPT FORMATION

Basic Types of Definition

The term "definition" is applicable to almost any answer to the question "what is x?" where "x" stands for any expression whose meaning remains constant. It is obvious that these answers can be of such different types that the term "definition" itself is ambiguous. The earliest distinction to be drawn, which is due to Aristotle and is still current today, is between *real* and *nominal* definition; real definition says what some *thing* is, nominal definition refers not to a thing but to a *sign*. In the nineteenth century various philosophers (including Wundt) tried to reduce all definitions to nominal definitions; but contemporary methodology distinguishes between the two kinds.

Further, certain distinctions are made among nominal definitions themselves. These may be either *syntactic* or *semantic*. In the first case the definition is simply a rule which permits the replacement of one sign with another (usually a shorter one). A semantic definition, on the other hand, fixes the meaning of the sign. The latter is again sub-divided into two types – *analytic* or lexical and *synthetic* or stipulative definitions. In an analytic definition a meaning is explicitly attributed to a sign, which is already appropriate to it in some way or other; the concept is therefore a pragmatic one, presupposing a meaning of the sign which is held in common by a group of people. A stipulative definition, on the other hand, gives the sign a new, arbitrarily chosen meaning. According to Robinson, the whole classification may be exhibited in the following schema:

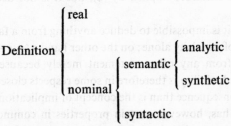

It should be observed that any condition which holds for a syntactic definition also holds *a fortiori* for all other kinds of definition, but not the other way round. It should also be observed, however, that a syntactic definition becomes a semantic definition when the system to which it belongs acquires an interpretation. We shall therefore begin by discussing syntactic definition in greater detail.

Types of Syntactic Definition

It is possible to distinguish between at least four different kinds of syntactic definition – and therefore *a fortiori* also of the other varieties: explicit, contextual, recursive and implicit definitions.

(1) *Explicit Definitions*. These are rules according to which an expression can simply be substituted for another; in most cases a shorter (often atomic) expression is substituted for a longer (molecular) one. By means of such a definition a new expression is introduced into the system. The technical convention in this case is to write down both expressions – the new one (the *definiendum*) and the old one (the *definiens*) – with a sign

of equality between them and "*df*" at the end of the whole expression or as a subscript to the sign of equality. Thus for example in the sentential logic of Łukasiewicz the implication sign "*C*" might be introduced by means of the following definition:

$$C = AN \quad df.$$

(2) *Contextual Definitions*. These are not rules but assertions, i.e. statements in the object language which are constructed in the following way: on the left-hand side is written a statement which contains a number of expressions already incorporated into the system, and also the definiendum; then follow the words "if and only if" and another statement, which consists only of expressions already incorporated into the system. The following statement might be an example of this kind of definition: "A man is *heroic* if and only if he performs acts which are (1) morally good, (2) very difficult and (3) extremely dangerous" – in which all parts of the statement except the word "heroic" are to be regarded as known.

(3) *Recursive Definitions*. Such definitions consist of a series of statements which are so constructed that each statement depends on all the preceding ones, and the definition is not complete until all the statements are given. This is best explained by an example: for this purpose we take the definition of "sentence" in the sentential logic of Łukasiewicz, already referred to:

1. "*p*", "*q*", "*r*" etc. are sentences;
2. an expression consisting of "*N*" followed by a sentence, is a sentence;
3. an expression consisting of "*C*", "*D*", "*E*" or "*K*" followed by two sentences is a sentence.

It is clear from this that in the system of Łukasiewicz the expression

$$CCpqCNqNp$$

is a sentence, since according to 1 "*p*" and "*q*" are sentences; hence from 2 "*Nq*" and "*Np*" are also sentences; it follows from 3 that "*CNqNp*" is a sentence (since it consists of "*C*" and the two sentences "*Nq*" and "*Np*"); also from 3 "*Cpq*" is a sentence; but the whole consists of a "*C*" (the first one) followed by two sentences (namely "*Cpq*" and "*CNqNp*"). Thus from 3 it is itself a sentence.

(4) *Implicit Definitions*. Cases in which the (syntactic) meaning of an expression is partly determined by a series of statements are also now

referred to as definitions. This happens when the expression to be defined occurs in each of a number of statements together with other expressions. In contrast to the case of contextual definition such statements do not need to be equivalents; they can, for example, be if–then statements, disjunctions etc.

Definition by Incorporation into the Axiomatic System

The last of the four kinds of syntactic definition is very important and deserves somewhat closer scrutiny. In this case the (syntactic) meaning of a sign is fixed in virtue merely of the fact that it occurs in the axioms of some system. This method (which was first dealt with by Burali-Forti) bears a certain resemblance to the Berlitz method of teaching languages. Take an unknown word, for example, "tar". What it means will gradually come to be understood as the following axioms are set forth: (1) the tar has two feet, (2) the tar speaks English, (3) the tar smokes a pipe. On the basis of 1 alone "tar" could mean a piece of furniture; 1 and 2 indicate that it is certainly alive, but it could still be a parrot; with all three axioms, however, it is clear that "tar" can mean only a human being. This example involves semantic meaning, but it should be obvious that syntactic meaning also is fixed by a system of axioms.

The fact that it is possible to define a sign by incorporating it into a system of axioms has as a counterpart the following very important rule: *the meaning of a sign which has been incorporated into an axiomatic system cannot be arbitrarily changed.* And conversely: if the axiomatic system is changed, the meaning of all the signs occurring in it is also changed. One might go even further, and maintain that *most signs not incorporated into any axiomatic system have no meaning at all.*

These rules are of crucial importance especially in the so-called formal sciences – mathematics and logic. It has been shown, for example, that the simple sign of negation ("not") can assume quite different meanings according to the system in which it is used. But they play a part in other sciences also, since there can be no science without a language and every language is an axiomatic system (though not always a carefully constructed one).

Semantic Definitions

A semantic definition is something quite different from a syntactic definition, i.e. from a rule of abbreviation, since through it the sign acquires meaning. This can come about, in principle, in two ways: (1) The meaning of the sign can be shown to another person by simply pointing; for example, if I wish to explain to someone the meaning of the word "cow" I can point to a cow and say the word at the same time. Such action is sometimes regarded as a definition, and in such cases we speak of *ostensive* definition (from the Latin *ostendere* = to show). (2) It is easy to see, however, that this method can be applied only in very rare cases; even the ostensive definition of adjectives and verbs offers difficulties, not to mention abstract terms such as the logical constants "and", "if", etc. In most cases, therefore, other signs whose meaning is already known have to be made use of. Such a definition, which will be called "*semantic*" *in the restricted sense,* consists in the establishment of a coordinating rule between two signs, the meaning of the first (the definiendum) being supposed unknown and that of the second (the definiens) taken as understood.

How is such a semantic definition to be constructed? It must clearly be formed in just the same way as a syntactic definition. As in that case, explicit, contextual, recursive and implicit definitions are to be distinguished. From the standpoint of techniques of definition there is no difference between the two types. But in the case of semantic definition only, a more complicated situation may arise, namely when rules for translating from one (unknown) language into another (known) language are laid down, since in this case a third (meta-)language has to be used. Moreover in this case, in contrast to purely syntactic definition, an interpretation of the system is presupposed.

Semantic definitions are subdivided into analytic and synthetic. Analytic definitions are used for making meanings which are already established more precise; synthetic definitions, on the other hand, attribute new meanings to the sign.

Both kinds can take all four forms mentioned above. It is true that there does not, at first sight, appear to be an implicit form of analytic definition, since in the system of axioms the sign acquires a new meaning. But this does not change the situation, since the meaning in question may be an already existing one.*

Synthetic definitions are often used in science today, not only because

---

* *Translator's note:* i.e. outside the axiomatic system in question.

new concepts have to be formed but also because the accepted meaning of words is too imprecise. Try, for example, defining such an apparently well understood word as "vegetable"!

A classic example of such difficulties is the concept of following logically from, i.e. the meaning of "if–then". No one has ever succeeded in defining it analytically, and the Stoics, to achieve a practicable definition, had already to resort to attributing a new meaning to the expression. But such a proceeding is dangerous, since the usual imprecise meaning will only too frequently come to mind when the term is used, leading to misunderstanding and error. More progress is possible with the introduction of artificial signs (such as technical terms in chemistry and astronomy), or abbreviated ones, as in mathematics.

Real Definition

While nominal definitions – of the syntactic or semantic kind – are particularly important for the mathematician and logician, students of the arts and sciences are concerned with them only incidentally, in as much as they also have to use a language. But their real interest is not so much in the clarification of the meanings of terms as in the understanding of things. This comes about chiefly through making statements about these things. But not all true statements have the same significance in science; there is rather a constant attempt to arrive at "fundamental" statements, starting from "superficial" ones. But this process is exactly what is now called "real definition".

Real definitions differ from one another in various respects. Robinson has tried to show that there are as many as twelve different meanings of the expression "real definition", but a number of these clearly refer to syntactic and semantic definition. It is possible, however, to distinguish between the following conceptions:

1. Specification of essence. This kind of definition is the goal of philosophers in the metaphysical and phenomenological traditions.

2. Specification of cause. This includes so-called genetic definitions, which characterize an object in terms of its origin.

3. Analysis of various aspects and constituent parts.

4. Specification of the laws which hold for a particular field. Giving this kind of definition amounts to forming the logical product of the scientific laws which belong to the field in question.

The three last-named types of real definition are to be found in most of the exact sciences; the first, on the other hand, is explicitly used only by philosophers of the metaphysical and phenomenological schools; it is not usual to talk about essence in the natural sciences. A closer examination of the way in which research proceeds in the natural sciences, however, shows that a kind of attempt is often made to devise an admittedly unattainable essential definition. Research penetrates ever more "deeply" into the structure of the object. For example, the answer to the question "What is light?" is different today from what it was in Newton's time, and even then it differed from what it was in the time of Galileo. We shall explain in the chapter on reductive methods how this hopeless pursuit of essential definitions in the sciences is conducted, since such definitions are statements which can be arrived at only by the reductive method.

16. EXAMPLE OF THE AXIOMATIC METHOD IN PRACTICE

Taking the sentential calculus as an example, we shall now demonstrate an axiomatic system. The method employed is the most rigorous of those available. Only the fundamentals (definitions, axioms, rules etc.) and one or two simple proofs are offered here.

AXIOMATIZATION OF THE SENTENTIAL LOGIC OF HILBERT AND ACKERMANN*

8.1. Primitive terms, rule of definition and formation-rules

8.11 Primitive terms: the dyadic functor D; the sentential variables p, q, r, s.**

8.12. Rule of definition: A new term may be introduced into the system through the construction of a group of terms to be called a "definition" consisting, in order, of the following elements: (1) an expression containing the new term together with other terms, all of which already belong

---

* From: I Bocheński – A. Menne: *Abriß der mathematischen Logik.* I am very grateful to Dr. Albert Menne for permission to reprint this passage. (*Translator's note:* Menne's work is a translation into German, with additions, of Bocheński's *Précis de logique mathématique.* An English version of the latter by Otto Bird (*A Precis of Mathematical Logic*) has been published by Reidel. Here I have translated from Menne's German.)
** In this passage, as also in 8.13, 8.33 and in the explanations of 8.51 and 8.52, the letters in italics should be enclosed between quotation marks; but no misunderstanding can arise if these are omitted.

to the system; (2) "="; (3) an expression consisting exclusively of primitive terms or of terms previously defined.

8.13. Formation rules: (1) a variable is a sentence, (2) a group of terms, consisting of N followed by a single sentence, is a sentence, (3) a group of terms, consisting of $A, B, C, D, E, J,$ or K followed by two sentences, is a sentence.

8.2. Definitions

8.21. $Np = Dpp$

8.22. $Apq = DNpNq$

8.23. $Cpq = ANpq$

8.24. $Kpq = NANpNq$

8.25. $Epq = KCpqCqp$

8.26. $Bpq = Cqp$

8.27. $Jpq = NEpq$

8.3. Rules of Deduction

8.31. Substitution rule: A sentence may be substituted for a variable, provided that the same sentence is substituted for every occurrence of the variable in the expression in question.

8.32. Rule of substitution by definition: An expression may be substituted for another expression in a sentence, when the two expressions are equivalent by definition, without being substituted for every occurrence of the latter expression in the same sentence.

8.33. Rule of detachment: If a sentence consisting of C followed by two sentences is a law of the system, and if the first of the two following sentences is a law of the system, then the second of the following sentences is also a law of the system.

8.4. Axioms

8.41. $CAppp$

8.42. $CpApq$

8.43. $CApqAqp$

8.44. $CCpqCArpArq$

8.5. Deductions

    8.44 $r/Nr \times 8.23\ p/r,\ q/p \times 8.23\ p/r = 8.51$

8.51. $CCpqCCrpCrq$

Explanation

The derivational line of theorem *8.51* is to be read as follows: "Take axiom *8.44*; replace *r* in it by *Nr*; apply to the result definition *8.23*, having first replaced *p* in this by *r* and *q* by *p*; apply definition *8.23* once again to the new result, this time having replaced *p* by *r*; this yields the theorem which was to be proved, namely *8.51*."

8.51 $p/App, q/p, r/p = C8.41 - C8.42 \ q/p - 8.52$

8.52. *Cpp*

Explanation

Having made the three substitutions in *8.51* which are indicated at the beginning, the expression

CCApppCCpAppCpp

is obtained, and this consists of (1) *C*, (2) *CAppp*, which is identical with *8.41*, (3) *C*, (4) *CpApp*, which is identical with *8.42* if *q* in the latter expression is replaced by *p*, and (5) the theorem *Cpp*, which we call *8.52*; this follows from the rest of the expression by a double application of the rule of detachment (*8.33*).

$\qquad 8.52 \times 8.23 \ q/p = 8.53$

8.53. *ANpp*

$\qquad 8.43 \ p/Np, q/p = C8.53 - 8.54$

8.54. *ApNp*

$\qquad 8.54 \ p/Np \times 8.23 \ q/NNp = 8.55$

8.55. *CpNNp*

$\qquad 8.44 \ p/Np, q/NNNp, r/p = C8.55 \ p/Np - C8.54 - 8.56$

8.56. *ApNNNp*

$\qquad 8.43 \ q/NNNp \times 8.23 \ p/NNp, q/p = C8.56 - 8.57$

8.57. *CNNpp*

$\qquad 8.44 \ q/NNp, r/Nq = C8.55 - 8.58$

8.58. *CANqpANqNNp*

$\qquad 8.51 \ p/ANqNNp, q/ANNpNq, r/ANqp = C8.43 \ p/Nq, q/NNp -$
$\qquad C8.58 - 8.59$

8.59. *CANqpANNpNq*

$\qquad 8.59 \ p/q, q/p \times 8.23 \times 8.23 \ p/Nq, q/Np = 8.60$

8.60. *CCpqCNqNp*

$\qquad 8.41 \ p/Np \times 8.23 \ q/Np = 8.61$

8.61. *CCpNpNp*

$\qquad 8.51 \ p/Apq, q/Aqp, r/p = C8.43 - C8.42 - 8.62$

8.62. $CpAqp$

    8.62 $q/Nq \times 8.23 \ p/q$, $q/p = 8.63$

8.63. $CpCqp$

    8.63 $q/Np = 8.64$

8.64. $CpCNpp$

    8.44 p/r, q/Apr, $r/q = C8.62 \ p/r$, $q/p - 8.65$

8.65. $CAqrAqApr$

    8.44 p/Aqr, $q/AqApr$, $r/p = C8.65 - 8.66$

8.66. $CApAqrApAqApr$

    8.51 $p/ApAqApr$, $q/AAqAprp$, $r/ApAqr = C8.43 \ q/AqApr - C8.66 -$
    8.67

8.67. $CApAqrAAqAprp$

    8.51 p/Apr, $q/AqApr$, $r/p = C8.62 \ p/Apr - C8.42 \ q/r - 8.68$

8.68. $CpAqApr$

    8.44 $q/AqApr$, $r/AqApr = C8.68 - 8.69$

8.69. $CAAqAprpAAqAprAqApr$

    8.51 $p/AAqAprAqApr$, $q/AqApr$, $r/AAqAprp = C8.41 \ p/AqApr -$
    $C8.69 - 8.70$

8.70 $CAAqAprpAqApr$

    8.51 $p/AAqAprp$, $q/AqApr$, $r/ApAqr = C8.70 - C8.67 - 8.71$

8.71. $CApAqrAqApr$

    8.44 p/Aqr, q/Arq, $r/p = C8.43 \ p/q$, $q/r - 8.72$

8.72. $CApAqrApArq$

    8.51 $p/ApArq$, $q/ArApq$, $r/ApAqr = C8.71 \ q/r$, $r/q - C8.72 - 8.73$

8.73. $CApAqrArApq$

    8.51 $p/ArApq$, $q/AApqr$, $r/ApAqr = C8.43 \ p/r$, $q/Apq - C8.73 - 8.74$

8.74. $CApAqrAApqr$

    8.51 $p/AqApr$, $q/AqArp$, $r/ApAqr = C8.72 \ p/q$, $q/p - C8.71 - 8.75$

8.75. $CApAqrAqArp$

    8.51 $p/ArApq$, $q/ArAqp$, $r/ApAqr = C8.72 \ p/r$, q/p, $r/q - C8.73 - 8.76$

8.76. $CApAqrArAqp$.

CHAPTER V

REDUCTIVE METHODS

17. GENERAL REMARKS

Historical Preliminaries

As in the case of most of the other branches of logic, the foundations of the theory of reductive methods of thought were laid by Aristotle. It is true that, at any rate in his logic, he took a much greater interest in deduction than in reduction, but he always made use of induction in the practice of science, and also discussed it theoretically in remarkable detail. In their modern form reductive methods were introduced by Bacon, whose "*tabulae*" represent the first attempt to establish the relevant rules. In Bacon's time and up to the middle of the nineteenth century, however, formal logic was unfortunately mistaken again and again for methodology, so that finally nearly every methodologist regarded it as his task to find a logic different from and better than deductive logic, namely so-called "inductive" logic.

In the nineteenth century significant inquiries were made in this area, especially in England, by Herschel and Mill among others. Herschel's basic ideas are still of importance today. The emergence of mathematical logic resulted in fresh points of view and led to further research in this field. Recent publications include those of Kneale, Braithwaite and von Wright.

The theory of probability and its applications form a particularly difficult chapter of reductive methodology which is being vigorously explored today. The publication of Keynes' work in 1927 was of paramount significance for these researches; another important work on reduction and the application of the theory of probability is that of Carnap (1951). But even so this whole field of inquiry has not yet been illuminated nearly as thoroughly as that of deductive methodology.

The Concept of Reduction and its Types

We have already exhibited the basic difference between deduction and reduction in connection with the work of Łukasiewicz. In deduction we infer the consequent from a conditional statement and its antecedent:

> if *A*, then *B*
> *A*
> therefore *B*.

In reduction, on the other hand, we infer the antecedent from a conditional statement and its consequent:

> if *A*, then *B*
> *B*
> therefore *A*.

We shall pass over for the moment the difficult problem of the justification of such a procedure – which clearly cannot be taken for granted – and restrict our attention briefly to a classification of types of reduction. There are two possibilities for this classification.

(a) In the first place, reduction, like deduction, can be subdivided into a progressive and a regressive type. In both cases the consequent is known to be true, but not the antecedent; if the reduction is to be done progressively, however, the antecedent – whose truth-value is still unknown – is taken as the starting-point, from which the argument proceeds to the known or ascertainable consequent. This progressive reduction is called "verification". Regressive reduction, on the other hand, begins with the known consequent and proceeds to the unknown antecedent. Regressive reduction is called "explanation". It is obvious that the familiar expression "hypothetico-deductive" refers to these two types of reductive method: the procedure is hypothetical, i.e. explanatory hypotheses are constructed (by regressive reduction), and deductive, because from these hypotheses verifiable consequences are derived (progressive reduction). Of course the expression "deductive" has a different sense here from the one we ordinarily give it.

(b) Another classification follows from a consideration of the nature of the antecedent: if it is a generalization of the consequent the reduction is called "induction"; if not we speak of *non-inductive reduction*.

Regressive Reduction and the Concept of Explanation

We shall deal first with regressive reduction, since it forms the first step in every reductive method. It is usually called "explanation". Since this term is ambiguous, its various meanings must first be specified.

Sometimes an explanation may be concerned with the meaning of a *sign*. This however is the province of definition, methods of which have already been discussed in the section on axiomatic method. In this case there is no reduction in our sense.

An explanation may, however, also be concerned with a statement – and thus with an objective proposition – the meaning of which is already known. This is the kind of explanation which interests us. It consists always of deriving the statement concerned from another statement. In general, therefore, "explain" in this sense means nothing other than constructing an axiomatic system, in which the statement to be explained is derived. And here once again two cases are possible: (a) The explanatory statement(s) is (are) already known to be true; (b) Its (their) truth-value is not yet known.

In the first case the task consists merely in the discovery of the statements needed for the explanation; in the second case these statements are constructed in the course of the explanation. The first type of explanation seems to occur frequently in historiography; one has, for example, a statement about the journey of a certain person, and would like to know why he undertook this journey: to this end one takes another statement already known to be true by historians, and shows that the statement about the journey which is to be explained is derivable from it. In this case, consequently, it is a matter of regressive deduction rather than of reduction. The second kind of explanation, on the other hand, is genuinely reductive.

So far we have spoken only of derivability, which is the minimal condition for an explanatory reduction. But not every reduction is based on a purely logical relationship between the explained statement and the explanatory one. "Causal" and "teleological" explanations may be appealed to if other relations hold between the two statements. We shall deal with these concepts later.

Verification

Once an explanatory statement has been made reductively, the next stage

93

is usually a so-called verification, i.e. an attempt to confirm or to reject it by means of progressive reduction. This is done as follows: from the statement that has been obtained reductively, and on the basis of some axiomatic system (usually not a purely logical one, but containing also a number of other statements obtained reductively) new statements are derived which are directly verifiable in the field concerned, i.e. the truth-value of which can be determined. The operations (experiments etc.) necessary to determine the truth-value of the derived statements are then actually carried out. If it turns out that they are true, this constitutes a confirmation of the statement from which they were derived. But if it turns out that they are false, this constitutes a falsification of that statement, which is then rejected.

This is a remarkable asymmetry. Falsification is logically valid, but confirmation on the other hand is never conclusive. In this case, as has already been pointed out, the inference from consequent to antecedent does not hold logically; whereas the inference from the negation of the consequent to the negation of the antecedent is based on a law of logic and is universally valid. It has therefore been said that the reductive sciences proceed essentially by negative rather than by positive steps, excluding spurious explanations one after another by a process of falsification.

The asymmetry is, however, not as acute as might appear at first sight. For in reduction nothing is ever derived from a *single* statement, say "*A*", which needs to be verified, but from a *conjunction* of this statement with others (perhaps with some theory, or the like) say "*T*". The schema is therefore not

> if *A*, then *B*
> not *B*
> therefore not *A*

but

> if *A* and *T*, then *B*
> not *B*

from which can be inferred only:

> therefore either not *A* or not *T*.

Theoretically, therefore, there is always a choice between the rejection of "*A*" and the rejection of "*T*". But in practice "*T*" is generally a statement of such importance that there is a strong inclination to reject "*A*", and to that extent the asymmetry persists.

The Reductive Sciences

The concept of reduction makes it possible to include a large number of sciences in the same category from the point of view of method. Among these are, first, the inductive sciences. The so-called empirical sciences form in their turn an important, but not the only, class of inductive sciences. It is well known that induction (in the authentic sense) is also applied in certain branches of mathematics, for example, in the theory of prime numbers.

The so-called historical sciences form another class. Without the concept of reduction it would be impossible to classify them at all: they are certainly not deductive, but they are not inductive either, since they do not lay down any general hypotheses or theories. The puzzle is solved when it is observed that they use reduction of the non-inductive variety. The same thing appears to be the case with some other sciences, including certain parts of geology, astronomy, geography etc.

Since among all these subclasses of science the class of natural sciences is the most comprehensive, and since the disciplines which belong to it possess a far better developed methodology than any of the others, we shall in what follows restrict attention almost exclusively to the methods applied in these sciences. They are at the moment the best available examples of reductive method.

18. THE STRUCTURE OF THE NATURAL SCIENCES

Protocol Statements

As was pointed out above the natural sciences form a subdivision of the so-called empirical sciences, to which the historical sciences also belong. The empirical sciences are characterized by the fact that in all of them statements about phenomena, that is, protocol statements, occur, and that in certain respects these form the essential foundation of the whole system. We shall first fix the meanings which are to be attached to the expressions "phenomenon" and "protocol statement".

Contrary to the usage of the phenomenologists, "phenomenon" is here taken to mean simply an event observable by the senses. The only point of controversy is whether this observation can be carried out entirely by external sense perception (sight, hearing, touch etc.). In one of the empirical sciences, psychology, some workers admit other methods of observation (introspection). But this is exceptional; in most of the natural sciences observations are made exclusively through the external senses; thus the fall of a body, the lighting of a lamp, a change in temperature etc. are regarded as phenomena, but not an event like the flow of electric current through a wire (as opposed to its observable results) or a disease as such (as opposed to its symptoms).

Statements which record the occurrence of phenomena are called "protocol statements" because they are written down in the protocol of the laboratory, observatory, or excavation, or in similar observational reports. A protocol statement usually incorporates the following details: spatial and temporal coordinates; the circumstances of the observation; a description of the phenomenon. In practice it also incorporates the name of the observer. A simple example is the note which a nurse makes of the temperature of a patient. This record might take the following form: Bed no. 47 (spatial coordinate); June 8, 1964, 7.15 a.m. (temporal coordinates); J. Smith (subject); in the mouth (circumstances); temperature: 38.7 °C (observed event).

Protocol statements also occur in non-empirical sciences, e.g. in philosophical cosmology, but they are used in the natural sciences in a special way which we shall now briefly discuss.

Development of the Natural Sciences

Viewed simply and schematically a natural science evolves more or less as follows: the point of departure is provided by *protocol statements* (this is a simplification; in fact, statements obtained reductively often lead to the protocol statements). At first protocol statements form a non-ordered class, which always has a tendency to grow larger, since research progresses and continually makes new observations. This class of protocol statements is the first stage in the development of a natural science.

The protocol statements are then explained by the assertion of (usually general) statements from which they are derivable, taking account of existing theories and on the basis of the laws of logic. As long as they are not verified, these are called *hypotheses*. After verification they become scientific *laws*. In this way the second level of scientific statements is constructed, namely a class of hypotheses or laws which are enunciated directly and reductively on the basis of protocol statements.

The next stage is an explanation of the laws themselves. This is done by forming a third level of statements from which the laws are derivable. If these statements are sufficiently general and explain many laws, they are usually called *theories* (the methodological terminology is still somewhat variable). The process which leads to the formation of theories is, from a logical point of view, basically the same as that which led to the enunciation of laws; but there are two differences:

(1) Laws are established (reductively) *directly* on the basis of protocol statements, whereas theories are established *indirectly;* they are based (reductively) on laws rather than on protocol statements.

(2) Laws are *generalizations* of protocol statements, i.e. they contain no extra-logical terms not already found in the protocol statements; whereas theories as a rule incorporate new "theoretical" terms (such as "neutron", "inflation", "unconscious" etc.) which are *not* found in the laws on which they are based. They are therefore *not mere generalizations* of the laws.

Theories, accordingly, can be explained in their turn, so that the logical structure of a natural science turns out to be a matter of many levels. For the sake of simplicity we consider only three levels: protocol statements, laws and theories.

It generally happens in the development of the natural sciences that observation continues to generate protocol statements, and explanation, accordingly, continues to construct new laws. Usually these new laws are "covered" at first by some theory already established, that is, they can be derived from such a theory. After a time, however, this theory is no longer adequate. In the early stages, as a rule, it is improved and modified so that it can continue to cover the new laws. Sooner or later, however, the time comes when it is impossible to extend it any further so as to explain all the new laws. Nevertheless it is still tolerated, as long as it is capable of explaining many laws. Finally, however, it becomes so complicated and inadequate that it has to be abandoned, being considered applicable at best to a limiting case. A new theory is sought for, and the whole process begins afresh. Neither the previous history of the natural sciences nor the logical analysis of their structure give any ground for supposing that this process will ever stop.

Verification

In this outline we have already mentioned an important element which has not yet been discussed in detail, namely the verification of hypotheses. In the construction of the natural sciences explanation and verification are used alternately. After the hypothesis which is to serve as the explanation of the protocol statement has been put forward there are derived from it protocol statements which do not yet exist as such, i.e. statements which have the form of protocol statements and whose truth-value is technically ascertainable, although it has not as yet been ascertained. The operations necessary to determine this truth-value are now carried out, i.e. the relevant experiments or other observations are performed, in order to obtain a confirmation or falsification. If the statements derived from the hypothesis prove to be true, then the hypothesis is regarded as confirmed and in certain circumstances becomes a law. But if it turns out that the statements are false, then the hypothesis is falsified and should be rejected – with the reservations mentioned above. In general the rule is that a hypothesis becomes a law if it (1) is confirmed by verification in a number of cases, (2) has not been falsified in any case.

From what has been said it is clear that hypotheses are of great importance for the guidance of observation and hence for the formation of protocol statements. Without them, in most cases, it would not be known what was really being looked for; they give a definite direction to observation. They are therefore the basis of every kind of experiment. Experimentation, without a guiding hypothesis, is inconceivable.

Experience and Thought

A few further remarks on the structure of the empirical sciences, as we have here presented it, may help to clarify the methodological situation.

(1) It is usually said, quite correctly, that experience forms the basis of the whole system of such sciences. More precisely: protocol statements ultimately determine the admissibility of other elements of the system in these disciplines. Anything inconsistent with the protocol statements must be set aside, anything which serves to explain these statements is admitted. It is this rule which determines the empirical character of these sciences.

(2) It does not by any means follow, however, that there could be a "purely empirical" science, in the sense in which this would consist

exclusively of protocol statements. That would be, not a science, but an unordered class of statements. It is not even true in an empirical science that apart from protocol statements only generalizations of them can occur. As we have said, theories normally contain expressions which do not occur in protocol statements at all. Every science consists of two kinds of statement: protocol statements based directly on experience, and hypotheses, laws, theories etc., that is, statements brought into being by thought and by means of reduction. We shall call the latter the "theoretical elements" of science.

(3) The expression "foundation" is ambiguous as it refers to the reductive sciences. From the logical standpoint a science is an axiomatic system in which just the most abstract theories, those furthest removed from experience, form the "foundation", i.e. the axioms, protocol statements being the final consequences of these theories. From the epistemological standpoint, however, protocol statements are primary, and theoretical elements and finally the most abstract theories are constructed (reductively) on the basis of these statements. To use a meataphor, one might say that a reductive science is an axiomatic system "stood on its head".

(4) Even epistemologically, however, laws and theories are not without importance. It would be naive to suppose that a scientist abandons a well-verified law when he finds one or two protocol statements which contradict it, or that he drops a broad theory covering many fields when it fails to account for a new law or two. It is clear, therefore, that while from the epistemological point of view protocol statements are the most important foundation of the system, they are certainly not the only one. Theoretical elements also play an important, although a secondary, role.

Schematic Representation

Two diagrams and a quite simple example may serve to clarify the foregoing account of the structure of the empirical sciences. The first diagram represents the psychological process; the arrows indicate the direction in which thought moves, not the order of logical derivability. The movement of thought goes from P_1^1 and P_2^1 to H_1 (regressive reduction; formation of hypotheses), then from H_1 to P_3^1 (verification); the same holds for H_2 with respect to P_1^2, P_2^2 and P_3^2. The theory T_1 is reached regressively from H_1 and H_2; then H_3 is derived from T_1 (together with relevant auxiliary theories, etc.) and thence P_1^3, which is the verifying protocol statement. The second diagram shows the logical structure of the finished theory; here all the arrows point downwards, since they indicate relationships of logical derivability. Thus H_1, H_2 and H_3 are derived from the theory T_1,

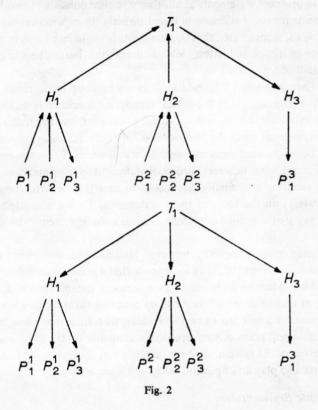

Fig. 2

and from H_1, H_2, and H_3 the corresponding protocol statements. A comparison of the two diagrams will show why we have called natural science an axiomatic system "stood on its head".

The Copernican Theory

The foregoing diagrams and descriptions may now be illustrated by a familiar example which has become fully intelligible only in the light of contemporary methodology, namely by a schematic outline of the

Copernican theory of the solar system. If we ask first what is the epistemological basis of this theory, the answer is: protocol statements, which
assert that certain points of light are to be found at certain places in the
apparent heavens at certain times. That is all. We cannot observe the
actual movement of the earth or the apparent movement of the stars. We
can only see points of light at this or that location in the sky.

Now to begin with the hypothesis is advanced that the points of light
move along a particular curve in the apparent heavens. This curve can be
represented by a mathematical function. If such a function is assumed it
becomes possible to deduce from it not only the statements already made
about the position of the point of light in question, but also predictions
as to the position of the same point at other times. We observe the
corresponding sector of the sky at the time ascertained by deduction
(calculation) and ascertain that the point in question is in fact found where
it ought to be according to the deduction. The hypothesis is thereby
verified, and becomes a law.

Gradually, therefore, there comes into being a whole class – a fairly
extensive class – of such laws. Once again there follows a reductive explanation of these, and this turns out to be the Copernican theory: we
suppose that the points of light are stars and planets, and that the planets
revolve around the sun along certain curves. This account is of course an
extreme simplification of the actual scientific process: in fact it involves a
highly complicated structure of mathematical statements, deriving partly
from geometry and physics, but partly from Copernican theory proper.
From this complex are derived by calculation all the laws which have
already been established and, in addition, some laws which have not yet
been established; and from these laws testable protocol statements about
events in the heavens. If these statements coincide with observation the
theory is verified. It is then formalized, and appears as an axiomatic
system of great power in which the Copernican theory, together with
other known mathematical and physical theories, provides the axioms,
the protocol statements being derived from these.

Examples of Verification

The example we have cited can be still further extended by reference to
more recent scientific developments, as follows.

Among the mathematico-physical theories which served for the derivation of astronomical laws in the Copernican system was Newton's theory of gravitation. As is well known, Einstein in 1915 opposed to this another theory which had the great advantage of being much simpler (it reduces gravitation to purely geometrical properties); and we shall see how important this greater simplicity is. In addition, however – and this is of primary interest to us here – Einstein's theory could be verified by means of protocol statements. On May 29, 1919, there was an eclipse of the sun, during which two expeditions (including one to Principe in the Gulf of Guinea under Eddington and Cottingham) were able to observe the phenomenon under especially favourable circumstances. The results were in complete agreement with the predictions derived from Einstein's theory.

Another classical example is the famous experiment of Michelson and Morley (1887). This was an attempt to verify the theory of Stokes and Kelvin, according to which there was an ether which served as a medium for the propagation of light. From this theory Michelson and Morley deduced that since the earth is in motion, there must be an "ether wind", and it followed that the speed of light must vary according to its direction in relation to this "ether wind". An experiment was carried out with complex apparatus in Cleveland, Ohio, from which it finally emerged that there is *no* detectable variation in the speed of light. The theory was therefore falsified.

The most interesting point here is that the theory was not immediately rejected, but that attempts were made to save it by various auxiliary theories. Michelson and Morley themselves believed that the ether moves with the earth. In 1895 Fitzgerald proposed the theory that the dimensions of the apparatus varied with the change of direction, and therefore that the variation in speed could not be observed. Only with Einstein's theory was it possible to offer a complete explanation of the new protocol statement.

19. TYPES OF EXPLANATORY STATEMENT

Introduction

The general structure of the reductive sciences is far more complex than that of the deductive ones. We have already seen that in the natural sciences at least three kinds of statement have to be distinguished: protocol statements, hypotheses (or laws), and theories. But in addition the statements of a reductive system, apart from protocol statements, can be divided into other classes. In this respect the older methodology now seems very inadequate. It shows a widespread tendency to reduce all these statements to a single type. For example, it was frequently maintained that every reductive or inductive explanation always came about through the establishment of so-called causal laws; again, others held that every explanation consisted in the specification of conditions. Similar monistic tendencies are not infrequently encountered still, although it is generally recognized that in the reductive sciences (and in some of the natural sciences) there are diverse kinds of laws and theories and also diverse kinds of explanation.

Since differentiation between the various kinds of explanation is important for an understanding of the reductive and also of the inductive method we shall briefly describe the most important of these as they are at present understood.

We distinguish between:

(a) causal and teleological explanation;
(b) concomitance laws and functional laws;
(c) deterministic and statistical laws.

Types of Condition

In general it may be said that reductive-explanatory statements always specify at least one condition governing the phenomenon which is to be explained: this is not to say that such a specification is sufficient in all sciences, but merely that whatever type of explanation may be chosen, it is always at the same time an explanation in terms of conditions. For example, if a teleological explanation is put forward which says that *A* is *B* because this leads to its also being *C*, not only has the objective of the state *AB* been specified but also the condition for its being the case.

Conditions may be sufficient, necessary, or necessary and sufficient.

(1) *Sufficient conditions.* We say that *A* is a sufficient condition for *B* if and only if the statement "if *A*, then *B*" is valid. It suffices in this case for *A* to be given in order for *B* also to be given.

(2) *Necessary conditions.* We say that *A* is a necessary condition for *B* if and only if the (inverse) statement "if *B*, then *A*" is valid. For in this case if *A* were not given, *B* could not occur; *A* is therefore a necessary condition for *B*.

103

(3) *Necessary and sufficient conditions.* We say that *A* is a necessary and sufficient condition of *B* when both the statements given above are valid, i.e. "*A* if and only if *B*".

It seems to be the case that all sciences ultimately aspire to the formulation of necessary and sufficient conditions. This is certainly true, for example, of classical physics. But in many cases one of the other kinds of condition has to suffice.

Every scientific classification offers a striking example of the first two kinds of condition. Such classification is based, obviously, on a series of laws, the so-called laws of concomitance. If we say, for example, that all mammals are vertebrates, this statement implies a law of concomitance, according to which a necessary condition of being a mammal is laid down, namely being a vertebrate. At the same time, however, a sufficient condition of being a vertebrate is also laid down, namely being a mammal, since it is sufficient for an animal to be a mammal in order to be a vertebrate as well.

An example of the third kind of condition is provided by chemical laws according to which a given substance has this or that property, e.g. such and such a specific weight.

Among contemporary methodologists it is beyond dispute that in the natural sciences many explanations take this last form. These are clearly not causal laws, since the phenomenon is not explained causally but rather formally (in the Aristotelian sense of the word).

Causal and Teleological Explanation

We have already remarked that in many sciences explanation by mere conditions does not suffice; often causal explanation, which consists in specifying the cause of the phenomenon is the prevailing mode. Two different concepts of cause, however, must be distinguished.

(1) *The ontological concept.* This concept can be roughly characterized as follows: the occurrence of *A* is the cause of the occurrence of *B* when *A* *brings about* the occurrence of *B* under the given circumstances. *A* here appears as an agent, which exerts an influence on *B*, in such a way as to make *B* happen.

Under the influence of Hume and his successors many methodologists maintain categorically that this concept of cause is never found in the natural sciences. But it can hardly be denied that many natural scientists (and not only psychologists and historians) do very often conceive of cause in this way in their explanations. Thus for example geologists think of the formation of mountains as caused quite explicitly by geotectonic factors, and caused furthermore in the ontological sense.

(2) *The phenomenalist concept.* In physics, however, and in a number of other highly developed sciences, the ontological concept of cause appears to have been eliminated, and for good reason. If it is assumed that the science in question is concerned only with protocol statements which describe phenomena observable by the senses, then any talk of an influence is obviously out of the question, since such a thing cannot be observed with the senses. It appears, therefore, that these sciences are limited to explanation in terms of conditions. But this is not in fact the case. It is true, as has been pointed out, that pure statements of conditions are often found, but these are still always spoken of as causes and as causal explanations.

What can these expressions mean? It seems that by "cause" is understood a (1) sufficient condition, which (2) precedes the caused event in time or at least is contemporaneous with it and further (3) stands in a certain spatial relationship to it. But this is neither distinct nor clear, and it is understandable why many contemporary methodologists prefer to eliminate this type of causality altogether and to speak only of conditions.

Even more controversial are so-called teleological explanations, which still crop up from time to time. They consist essentially of stating the purpose of the phenomenon to be explained. For example, if the remarkable structure of certain flowers is explained by saying that it ensures their fertilization, the explanation is of this type. From the logical standpoint such an explanation runs counter to causal explanation, since, although it specifies a phenomenal condition, this condition involves a phenomenon which *has not yet occurred* and which does not appear in time until after the phenomenon which is to be explained.

In physics and the other sciences which deal with inanimate nature teleological explanations are no longer appealed to; in the biological sciences causal explanation appears to predominate, but teleological explanation also turns up here and there, for example in the question of the adaptation of the various organs of the body to their respective uses. There are similarly teleological tendencies in sociology, although there too the main pattern is causal.

Teleological explanations involve difficult philosophical problems; the most important question is how something which has not yet occurred and which therefore does not exist can explain a phenomenon which does exist. We shall pass over this problem here, as over other philosophical problems which are out of the reach of pure methodology.

Functional Laws

In the highly developed sciences – not only in physics but also in psychology – so-called functional laws are laid down. They are always of the following form: for all A, F and G – where F and G are properties of A – the magnitude of F is a (mathematical) function of the magnitude of G. A simple and classical example is the law of falling bodies: the velocity of a falling body is a function of the time it has taken to fall.

How can such laws be interpreted logically? They are statements which involve a *double generalization:* in the first place there is a reference to *all A,* i.e. to all falling bodies, just as in the case of a non-functional law; but to this is added another generalization: the mathematical function, that is to say, involves the generalization that all magnitudes of one kind are coordinated in a certain way with magnitudes of the other kind.

Fundamentally, therefore, functional laws are merely a complicated form of conditional laws. In this connection it should be pointed out that the condition in question can be of any of the three kinds mentioned above. In practice, however, every science strives to establish functional laws which specify necessary and sufficient conditions of the phenomenon in question.

The establishment of functional laws forms the main task of quantitative induction. Unfortunately this part of general methodology has not as yet been fully worked out theoretically, although every natural science which establishes such laws has its own methods of doing so.

Statistical Laws

Until a few decades ago statistical laws were applied almost exclusively in the social sciences: today they are used in many other fields. They are concerned with statements not about individuals but about classes of individuals; in statistical laws it is asserted that property B is found in a certain proportion of the members of a class A, e.g. in 60% of all cases. A simple example is the statistical law of mortality which says that of every 1000 human beings born alive n will die in their kth year.

Such laws are also called "indeterministic" since nothing definite (determinate) is asserted of single individuals; e.g. from the assertion that of every 1000 Frenchmen born alive precisely 138 die in their 47th year nothing follows with respect to the death of my friend Jean-Paul, who happens to be in his 47th year: he may die and he may not. In such cases we speak, therefore, of a probability, which is precisely calculable mathematically. But the exactness of this calculation must not deceive us as to its results, it cannot alter the fact that, as far as the individual is concerned, we cannot know whether the event in question will happen to him or not.

It is therefore clear that statistical laws do not form a special variety *alongside* the other kinds; what is put forward in statistical form may just as well be a conditional explanation as a causal one, and for that matter there are also statistical functional laws.

It is to be noticed that non-statistical laws can be regarded as limiting cases of statistical ones, namely as laws according to which the phenomenon in question occurs in 100% of the cases.

20. INDUCTION

Authentic and Spurious Induction

Induction is an important form of reduction which is used chiefly in the natural sciences. In the first place a distinction has to be made between authentic induction and various methods which are also called "induction" but are not reductions.

(1) So-called mathematical induction is a case of spurious induction. It consists in the application of the following rule: If F holds for 1, and if it is also the case that if it holds for n then it holds also for $n + 1$, then F holds for every number. Such "inductions" are very common in mathematics but it ought to be clear that they are really pure deductions. The term "induction" is misleading here.

(2) Further, reference is sometimes made to so-called "complete" induction. In this case the following rule is applied: if $x_1, x_2, x_3 \ldots x_n$ are elements of a class a, and are *all* its elements (i.e. so that there is no element in this class apart from them), and if F holds for $x_1, x_2, x_3 \ldots x_n$, then F holds for all the elements of a. This also is not an authentic induction but a kind of deduction; there is, that is to say, a law in mathematical

logic on the basis of which this rule can be infallibly established. Incidentally its application is sometimes useful, but it is not practicable in the natural sciences, because they generally deal with infinite classes and an infinite number of things can never be observed.

(3) It should be observed further that Aristotle used the corresponding term not only for a kind of inference but also for abstraction, that is, for a method of forming concepts. Even today some philosophers still use it in this way; but the method they have in mind clearly has little in common with scientific induction.

The term "authentic induction" is reserved here first of all for a process of inference, that is a method of thought by means of which *statements* are made; secondly for a process which is essentially ampliative, i.e. one which proceeds not only from the totality of the individuals to the general (as in complete induction) but from *some* individuals, which do not comprise all the elements of the class in question, to the general. Such a process obviously poses a special methodological problem: What is the justification for making such a transition? This is the so-called problem of induction. As early a thinker as Aristotle demonstrated with admirable acuteness that induction is not conclusive, and his proof of this has not as yet been contradicted. And yet induction is not only constantly used in everyday life but also forms one of the main methods of the natural sciences. On what grounds?

The various attempts which have been made to solve these difficult philosophical problems cannot be discussed here; it is enough to point out that certain methodological questions are involved. It is not the intention of this outline to justify individual methods, but merely to describe the methods which are used in contemporary scientific practice and discussed by methodologists.

Types of Induction

Inductions which we call "authentic" may be classified as follows:

(1) With respect to their object, into *primary* and *secondary* induction. The former leads to hypotheses or laws, the latter to theories.

(2) With respect to the type of explanatory statement, into *qualitative* and *quantitative, deterministic* and *statistical* induction, according as the statement concerns only a concomitance of phenomena, or a functional dependence of one on the other, and as these again are invariable or

statistical. As has already been said, little theoretical work has been done so far on the methods of quantitative induction.

(3) With respect to the method itself, into *enumerative* and *eliminative* inductions. Enumerative induction simply accumulates statements which can be derived from the explanatory statement in question; the important thing in this case is therefore the number of such statements. In the case of eliminative induction, however, statements about individual cases (such as protocol statements) need not be multiplied, but rather possible hypotheses are eliminated which might apply to the given case. In this second method the number of statements taken into consideration is not important, but their *kinds*, i.e. the variety of the phenomena recorded, is important. The "tables" of Francis Bacon, and Mill's methods, are special ways of applying eliminative induction.

It is generally recognized today that pure enumerative induction is very seldom used – it even tends sometimes to be called "unscientific". On the other hand, methodologists are not agreed as to how the other type of induction should be conceived. Whereas von Wright, for example, holds that it is entirely eliminative, Braithwaite holds that elimination plays a progressively less important role in the practice of science, the progress of which results more from confirmation than from falsification (i.e. elimination).

Mill's Methods

Although they are outdated and have never been used in science as they were conceived by Mill, we shall discuss these methods briefly because they help in the understanding of what really happens in the process of inductive inference.

Mill puts forward five such methods; we shall summarize his account, rendering what he calls "cause" as "condition" and assuming, for the sake of simplicity, that there are only two classes of phenomena, each with only three elements: *a, b, c* and *A, B, C*.

(1) *Method of Agreement: a* occurs in association with *AB* and also in association with *AC*. Assuming that (1) there *is* a condition for the occurrence of *a* and (2) *A, B,* and *C* are the *only* possible conditions, it follows that *A* is a sufficient condition for *a*.

(2) *Method of Difference: a* occurs in association with *ABC,* but not in association with *BC* (where only *A* is missing); with the same assumptions it follows that *A* is a necessary condition of *a*.

109

(3) *Joint Method of Agreement and Difference: a* occurs in association with *AB* and in association with *AC* but not in association with *BC;* again with the same assumptions it can be inferred from this that *A* is a sufficient and necessary condition for *a.*

(4) *Method of Residues:* from other inductions it has been established that *B* is a condition of *b,* and *C* a condition of *c; abc* occurs in association with *ABC.* With the former assumptions and with the further assumption that each phenomenon can be the condition of only *one* type of phenomenon, it follows that *A* is a necessary and sufficient condition of *a.*

(5) *Method of Concomitant Variation: A* changes in the same way as *a,* but *B* and *C* do not change in this way. This is a method of quantitative induction, which will be dealt with below; for the moment it can be passed over.

In the case of the first four methods at least two assumptions must be taken into account, namely that there should be a condition of the type in question at all, and further that only one of the phenomena enumerated (in our example *A, B,* and *C*) can be this condition. The first of these assumption is called the "deterministic" postulate, and the second is sometimes called the "closed-system" postulate. If they are assumed then the conclusions follow *deductively.* But it may well be asked how such assumptions can possibly be justified. In fact not only do they have no justification, but they must often be acknowledged to be completely false.

The Presuppositions of Mill's Methods

It should be remarked at once that the determinism under discussion here is not *ontological* determinism; ontological causality is unknown in the natural sciences and so therefore is determinism in this sense (from which incidentally it follows that it is absurd to try to deduce the freedom of the will from the rejection of methodological determinism). But even if attention is restricted to phenomenal determinism (that is to conditions, not ontological causes) the expression is still ambiguous. *Strict determinism* applies only to the case of the combined method, since only in this case is there assumed to be a necessary and sufficient condition for every phenomenon. In the method of difference there is assumed to be only a *necessary* condition for every phenomenon, i.e. it is assumed that a certain other phenomenon is always necessary, but not that the occurrence of this phenomenon is sufficient for the occurrence of the one in question. In this case we speak of *partial determinism*. This is an accepted presupposition of contemporary microphysics: in order for a particle, e.g. an electron, to be set in motion, certain conditions have to be fulfilled; but these are not sufficient, since, even if they are fulfilled, the expected phenomenon may not occur.

How can the postulation of one or another kind of determinism be justified? Certainly not by reference to ontology. This can show that every phenomenon has a *cause,* but not that this cause is a *phenomenon.* Logic cannot provide such a principle either. It cannot be established inductively, since it is presupposed in every induction. In these simple observations lies the heart of the so-called problem of induction, and they are sufficient to show that every attempt to transform induction into deduction by the addition of new premises is bound to fail.

The same is true of the second postulate; there are no grounds, ontological or logical or inductive, for the assumption that the hypotheses put forward by us are the only possible ones. On the contrary we know from experience that many other hypotheses are also possible.

These observations confirm what has already been said about determinism: there is no bridge between induction and deduction, at any rate not in the form of additional premises.

Certain methodologists, to pursue this point briefly, have attempted to establish such a connection in a different way. They have maintained that induction can be transformed into deduction by simply redefining the phenomenon in question. As an example take diamond, and suppose it to have been defined hitherto by three properties *A, B* and *C;* now suppose somebody burns one or two diamonds, as Lavoisier did, finds that carbon monoxide (CO) is obtained from the combustion, and therefore claims that all diamonds are made of carbon. How can this be justified? Simply by adding the newly discovered property "being made of carbon" to the previously known qualities: "diamond", according to the new definition, will now mean everything which has the properties *ABC* and also the newly discovered property of being made of carbon. If this is agreed upon it follows deductively that a diamond must always be made of carbon.

But it is obvious that such a purely conventional method cannot be taken seriously in science. It can be carried through consistently, but it

111

leaves the question unanswered why *ABC* should always be associated with the new property. A convention is not a natural law, and science requires more serious foundations.

Induction and System

A closer examination of the way in which scientists actually proceed in the establishment of laws shows that the decisive factors are not Mill's assumptions but something quite different, namely the simplicity of the laws and their interconnectedness in an axiomatic system. The axiomatic interconnectedness may be illustrated by a simple example. If it is known that everybody who was born before a certain year has died, this is sufficient to establish the hypothesis that all men are mortal. But this hypothesis becomes much more convincing if it is also known – from other inductions – that men are vertebrates and that all vertebrates are mortal. In this way the hypothesis is not only induced from protocol statements but also derived from a general law, and it emerges considerably strengthened. This interconnectedness with other laws and with the whole of the scientific system concerned is a factor which in every case considerably increases the plausibility of a hypothesis. Some methodologists go so far as to make it a necessary condition for the transformation of a hypothesis into a law, and still others hold that it is the only basis on which scientific hypotheses can be made at all. This last position is certainly exaggerated, but it is beyond question that their interconnectedness in an axiomatic system does play an important role in the recognition of hypotheses.

Sometimes, however, hypotheses are used which do not stand in this kind of relationship; these are so-called working hypotheses, which are not called "laws". They are used as a matter of expediency in the investigation of a particular, limited field. Thus, for example, the well-known ethnologist P. W. Schmidt has used historical materialism effectively as a working hypothesis, though he himself found that there was no wider system in connection with which it could be used.

The Rule of Simplicity

This further common assumption may be formulated as follows: if several hypotheses explain a given statement, then the simplest among them should be chosen. This rule is necessary in order to move forward in circumstances where there are in principle infinitely many possible hypotheses, by reducing them to a single one. That the class of hypotheses is often infinite may be shown by the following example: Consider three points on a plane which stand for three protocol statements (concerning e.g. the pressure of a gas in an enclosure); the problem is to find a curve

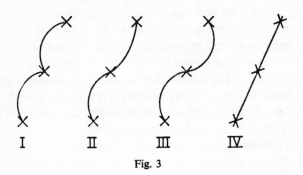

Fig. 3

on which they can lie. The mathematical function corresponding to this curve will be the explanatory hypothesis. It is clear that there exists an infinite class of such curves; the accompanying diagram gives just a few examples. In this case we shall certainly choose the last curve, namely the straight one, because it is the simplest.

Summary. Philosophical Interpretations

To sum up, we may say that at least four postulates are necessary for the application of qualitative induction: the postulate of determinism, the closed-system postulate and the postulates of interconnectedness and of simplicity. Four corresponding rules may then be set up: look for determining conditions; assume that these conditions, when found, must belong to a given system; choose the hypotheses best interconnected with the system as a whole; choose the simplest hypothesis.

How can these rules be justified? Philosophers have argued about this for centuries. One suggestion has been that their justification is intuitive: according to this we understand the laws of nature by a sort of intuition as well as by rational inferences. According to another explanation, the Kantian, these laws are to be conceived as forms of our thought, which we impose upon Nature, so that Nature itself is in fact formed by them. The pragmatists, on the other hand, maintain that induction is at bottom a purely practical affair, by means of which we simply get the most service-able predictions we can. Finally the pure sceptics, of whom there are a good many, hold that inductively-established statements have no truth-value at all.

It should be clear from what has gone before that all these views are mistaken. There is no such thing as an intuition of natural laws, nor are they given a priori; on the contrary it is evident that we reach our con-clusions only by difficult rational work, and then not always with cer-tainty. The idea that the natural sciences are concerned only with practical affairs is contradicted by the fact that, *in order to be* practical, a statement based on induction must already be true, i.e. it must correspond to the real state of affairs. Finally scepticism is weakened by the practical successes of technology: How could our laws be so regularly confirmed if they had no positive truth-value? It is also worth remarking that through all the changes of theory that have taken place, and in spite of the progress of the sciences and the more stringent demands this has brought with it, many laws have remained essentially stable.

There may, to put it briefly, have been some success in understanding certain aspects of Nature with the aid of the inductive method; but no one has as yet been able to say how this is possible. The great work achieved by induction appears to the logician like the successful deciphering of a text in code, to which we still lack the key. That some things have been decoded seems certain; it is just that we do not know how this has happened.

21. PROBABILITY AND STATISTICS

The Two Meanings of "Probability"

Most methodologists now accept the view that the term "probability" and similar expressions not only have very diverse meanings in everyday usage but also often mean two or more quite different things in technical language. This may be clarified by the following consideration: Many scientific laws are probability laws, i.e. they merely assign probabilities to events. These laws are, however, themselves only probable (because they rest on induction). The term therefore has two different meanings: the probability of an *event* and the probability of a *hypothesis* (or of a law or a theory).

The chief difference between the two concepts consists in the fact that it is possible, at least in principle, to express the first probability numerically: it makes sense to say that the probability of an event has such and such a value. On the other hand the probability of a hypothesis cannot be determined numerically. It seems nonsensical to say that Einstein's theory or Boyle's law has a probability of 3/4, and so on. The first kind of probability is therefore usually called "numerical", "mathematical" or "statistical" probability, while the second is called "acceptability" or "credibility".

Statistics

Every probabilistic hypothesis, like other reductively established statements, has as its ultimate basis nothing but protocol statements. But a probabilistic hypothesis is not directly based on such individual statements, but is mediated by statistics. By this is understood simply a numerical treatment of cases in which two kinds of phenomenon appear together (simultaneously or in a certain temporal order). A statistical statement is therefore always of the following form: Among m cases of a phenomenon of type A, n cases are also of type B. A concrete example might be: Among 3567 inhabitants of town X there are 78 foreigners. It should be clear that every simple statistical result calls for two operations carried out one after the other: (1) recording the protocol statements and (2) counting them.

The work of the statistician is not, however, limited to this. The information gathered has to be put into a form which makes possible a sure and convenient application of reductive methods: e.g. it may be expressed in percentages from which it is possible to find mean values. But this often involves complicated mathematical processes (there are various concepts of the mean value and highly refined methods of arriving at it). Finally the statistician must pay special attention to the elimination of errors in the original statements by the use of further mathematical methods.

In the collecting of data for statistical purposes the following rule is very significant. It is often possible to cover not the whole field (the whole population) but only a sample of it. In this case it is important that the class of phenomena sampled should be as representative as possible of the whole, in the sense that it has the same composition as the whole. But, according to the fundamental laws of the theory of probability, this can be achieved only on condition that the distribution of chosen cases should be neutral and random. Every precaution should be taken to ensure that the

115

selection is made without bias. An example: in order to find out, by taking a selection of names from the Telephone Directory, how many Londoners are foreigners, it would be wrong to choose only from the names which begin with "Z", since among them it is obvious that there are comparatively more foreign names than elsewhere. The names chosen must be uniformly distributed through the book as a whole.

Interdependence of Phenomena

In general the researcher who is using the inductive-statistical method is concerned not with two, but with at least three classes. First of all there is a comprehensive class of phenomena, e.g. the class of children in Zurich. This contains two subclasses, e.g. the class of children who have been vaccinated and the class of children suffering from the illness against which the vaccination was performed. The question is whether and to what extent the two subclasses are dependent on one another, i.e. whether vaccination prevents the illness or not. The figures supplied by statistics may in this very simple case be represented in the following table:

Class of Children	ill	well
vaccinated	x	y
not vaccinated	z	t

The variables "x", "y", "z" and "t" may be thought of as replaced by figures.

The first question is: in what relation would the values x, y, z and t stand to one another if being ill and being vaccinated had no connection at all, i.e. if being vaccinated was not a condition for being well and being ill was not a condition for not having been vaccinated. A simple consideration will show that in this case the ratio of ill children who have been vaccinated (x) to all the children who have been vaccinated ($x + y$) must be the same as that of all the ill children ($x + z$) to all the children accounted for ($x + y + z + t$), i.e.

$$x:(x+y)=(x+z):(x+y+z+t).$$

But this formula reduces by simple algebraic operations to

$$xt = yz$$

What happens, however, if vaccination has a positive influence on the disease?* Then the ratio of ill children who have been vaccinated (x) to all the children who have been vaccinated ($x + y$) will be greater than that of all the ill children ($x + z$) to all the children being investigated ($x + y + z + t$). A mathematical operation analogous to the previous one leads to the formula:

$$xt > yz.$$

In the converse case, if vaccination has a negative effect on the disease (which should normally be the case) the result will be:

$$xt < yz.$$

The two last mentioned formulae are examples of statistical laws of a very simple type.

Tables of Correlation

In what follows a somewhat more complicated form of the statistical treatment of phenomena is dealt with briefly – namely so-called tables of correlation. With their help functional laws are established. In this example there are again a main class and two subclasses: the class of plants, A, the subclass of fertilized plants, B, and the subclass of fertilized plants which have grown, C. In contrast to the previous example each subclass is again divided into five further subclasses, according to the amount of fertilizer used and the degree of growth respectively. Observations yield the following table:

	C_0	C_{10}	C_{20}	C_{30}	C_{40}
B_0	x_{00}	x_{01}	x_{02}	x_{03}	x_{04}
B_{10}	x_{10}	x_{11}	x_{12}	x_{13}	x_{14}
B_{20}	x_{20}	x_{21}	x_{22}	x_{23}	x_{24}
B_{30}	x_{30}	x_{31}	x_{32}	x_{33}	x_{34}
B_{40}	x_{40}	x_{41}	x_{42}	x_{43}	x_{44}

"B_n" ("B_0", "B_{10}" etc.) means that the plants in this subclass were given n units (grams) of fertilizer, "C_n" ("C_0", "C_{10}" etc.) that they grew n units (millimetres). Each "x" with a double subscript is a variable for which a number has to be substituted by counting cases. The two subscripts simply indicate the row and the column respectively.

* *Translator's note:* i.e. makes it worse.

117

If now the fertilizer has a positive effect on growth, it holds that the more fertilizer, the greater the growth. Let us take the simplest possible case: growth is directly proportional to quantity of fertilizer. Clearly in the first row x_{00} will be greater than x_{01}, this will be greater than x_{02}, etc. In the second row x_{11} will be greater than x_{10} or x_{12}, but the latter will be greater than x_{13}, and this in turn greater than x_{14}. In the third row x_{22} must be greater than x_{20} or x_{24}. In general the following pattern emerges: The greatest numbers will lie along the main diagonal – in our example x_{00}, x_{11}, x_{22}, x_{33}, x_{44}; the two adjacent diagonals will have smaller numbers (x_{10}, x_{21}, x_{32}, x_{43} and x_{01}, x_{12}, x_{23}, x_{34}), and the nearer we get to the corners (x_{40} and x_{04}) the smaller the numbers will be. To put it briefly: there is a concentration of cases in the region of the diagonal $x_{00} - x_{44}$ and an attenuation in the direction of x_{40} and x_{04}.

All this can also be dealt with mathematically. There are formulae (which can be graphically represented) which give the "normal" distribution of cases in such a table of correlation.

It is not our task to describe the related mathematical methods and formulae. Only the most elementary treatment of the principles of the statistical method, as far as possible without the use of mathematics, is called for here.

Correlation and Probability

What is the outcome of the application of this method? Basically all it amounts to is a collection of protocol statements: so and so many cases of the association of such and such magnitudes of two phenomena in a *finite* class. How, from this purely factual account, can we arrive at a universal law covering an unlimited number of cases – every case, in fact, of the phenomena in question?

Two different problems must be distinguished here:

(1) Can anything be concluded from a table of correlations as to whether and how an individual phenomenon will turn out – for example how many millimetres a given plant will grow if it gets a certain amount of fertilizer? The answer is that even if the phenomenon is one of those already observed, i.e. represented in the table – excluding cases where a direct observation is possible or where the protocol statement in question is still available – only a *probability* can be derived from the table. In our example this is simply a case of so-called relative frequency: if out of m

plants having received k grams of fertilizer n have grown p millimetres, the probability that another plant (also having received k grams of fertilizer) will grow p millimetres is equal to n/m. This means, however, that with respect to a certain individual we know nothing, but only something with respect to the whole class. This of course is enough by way of data for the accurate calculation of rates of insurance, for example, without having to take account of individual cases.

(2) Can anything be concluded from a table of correlations about all the phenomena, even the unobserved (i.e. future) ones, belonging to the class in question? This second problem has nothing further to do with probability in the sense discussed above. The logical structure of the inductive process in this case is exactly the same as the one already considered in connection with Mill's methods. What comes into play here is determinism, the closed-system postulate, and the postulates of interconnectedness and simplicity – the latter, of course, only if a functional law is to be constructed.

22. HISTORICAL METHOD

Natural Science and History

It is usually said that there are two fundamental differences between the natural sciences and history. (1) The first have as their object non-mental (material) things and events, the object of the second is mental. (2) Whereas the natural sciences set up atemporal laws, disregarding historical considerations, it is characteristic of history on the other hand that it deals with past events, and deals with them as such.

Neither of these criteria, however, is very useful if the intention is to distinguish clearly between the two fields. For (1) man, whose activities are discussed by the historical disciplines, obviously does not consist exclusively of mind, but is also material; and it is not always easy to determine how far in a particular situation he acts on a mental level. Do economic matters, for example, which man shares to a certain extent with the animals, belong to the realm of mind or of matter? And yet history deals with economic phenomena. On the other hand psychology certainly cannot be counted as history although it quite definitely deals in part with mental objects. (2) The second criterion is also inadequate: there are various natural sciences which discuss the past, and discuss it as such.

119

Russell has observed that the phenomena with which physics deals are always past phenomena, but just recently past, whereas history deals with the more distant past. The difference is therefore only one of degree.

The difference in method is clearer. It is a striking fact that no historical discipline makes general statements. Such statements are, it is true, made use of in historical work, but the hypotheses and laws established with their help are always singular: Why did Napoleon begin his campaign against Russia so late? Because he was unable to assemble the necessary supplies quickly enough. Why did Alexander invade India? The explanation is to be found in his upbringing, etc. Here we are always dealing with explanation, i.e. with a reductive process. In no case is induction involved.

Many methodologists of the so-called humanities (to which in a certain sense all historical disciplines belong) also maintain that these disciplines are not explanatory at all, but simply descriptive, and thus quasi-phenomenological, although without the exclusion of existence. But this is obviously wrong. Contemporary humanistic (historical) disciplines do not only describe, they also explain. It appears that these methodologists, forced to make a choice between deduction and induction, see no way out but to take the position referred to. But we know that not every explanation is necessarily inductive. From the methodological standpoint history is characterized most exactly as a reductive, non-inductive science.

Point of Departure

Historical disciplines are empirical sciences. They are based on statements about phenomena in the "scientific" sense of the word, that is observable processes. The fact that the phenomena belong to the past does not alter the situation. In the natural sciences themselves this situation is not only conceivable, but actually obtains. But it does materially complicate the reductive process. For whereas the natural scientist usually has protocol statements at his disposal which have been formulated in precise language by research workers from his own culture, the *interpretation* of which conceals no difficulties in principle, the historian is compelled to begin with documents, which are not in the least like protocol statements as the scientist knows them. The sources of history, often written in an unfamiliar language, come only too often from a culture which is foreign to the historian. Behind the words there lies, for the most part, a completely unknown set of axiomatic relationships. Furthermore, the credibility of the documents is always questionable. These are not sober reports from the laboratory made by experts whose professional standards (and whose commitment to a scientific career) usually provides an adequate guarantee of honesty.

It is therefore clear that in history what corresponds to protocol statements is not found at the beginning, but has to be acquired by a long and often difficult process of interpretation. It is only by this means that statements of fact can be obtained, whether reductively or deductively. This constitutes a further fundamental difference between historical and other scientific disciplines.

This state of affairs may also be expressed as follows: the historical sciences, like the natural sciences, incorporate the two logical stages of statements about individual phenomena and explanatory statements. But there is in them also a further stage, which *precedes* the stage of protocol statements, namely of statements taken directly from the documents. The pattern of the historical sciences is therefore: documents – factual statements – explanatory statements.

Choice of Data

There is a further difference between the sciences in question. The mass of documents and of the facts recorded in them is so enormous that one of the historian's first tasks is to make a wise choice from it. Admittedly the natural scientist is also confronted with a great number of protocol statements and perhaps an even greater number of phenomena. But thanks to his inductive method (i.e. in virtue of the tendency to make general statements) his choice is much easier, since he is interested only in what can be generalized. The historian on the other hand is faced with an unmanageable mass of documents, without any such principle to guide him. It is clear, for instance, from a consideration of the history of the first World War, that it is impossible to take account simultaneously of the many thousands of reports, the records of diplomats and general staffs, the memoirs, the books and articles etc. The historian must choose between them.

Two problems stand out as specific to history. The first is philosophical in nature: why will the historian not use induction? Two answers are given to this question. The first, which is due in essentials to Windelband, runs: the object of historical science, namely human affairs, is so constituted that interest is centred on the individual rather than the general. For example, what Napoleon or St. Francis had in common with other men is irrelevant; the important thing is what was uniquely personal about them. Therefore the historical sciences are *idiographic* disciplines (describing properties) not *nomothetic* (establishing laws), and induction is of no use to them. The second answer appeals to the great complexity of historical phenomena, which makes it impossible to establish general laws. History therefore remains on a low level, collecting protocol statements and making individual explanations. It is capable of developing into an inductive science, however – sociology is one example of this development – and historical writing as such may be regarded simply as a preliminary stage. The point of view represented by this second answer is sharply criticized, and rejected, by most historians today.

The second problem is methodological in nature; what rule determines the choice of documents? To this purely methodological question there is, as far as I know, no clear answer. The documents form, as has been said, the starting-point of historical research. Admittedly, anyone who puts forward, and tries to verify, a hypothesis, has to that extent a guiding principle; but the question as to the rule of choice is posed again for the hypothesis itself. It seems, therefore, that ultimately the selection involves a subjective evaluation. For this reason history, as opposed to the natural sciences, is said to be "value-laden". This does not mean, however, that history is subjectively determined as far as the truth of its results is concerned. Free choice affects only the selection of phenomena. Once this has been made, the further treatment proceeds no less objectively than in the natural sciences.

Interpretation

The "style" of contemporary historical work is loose; value is attached mainly to the elegance of the presentation. If however we examine not the form but the methods of thought which are embodied in it we find that, in documentary research, the semiotic method is principally used with assistance from axiomatics (axiomatization), though not with the same strictness as in logic or mathematics. Priority is given to the critical examination of texts, which are often spoiled by errors of transcription, the aim being to restore the original text. This requires in some parts the use of very complicated methods, partly reductive and partly even deductive; statistics can also play an important role in it.

It is only after this that serious interpretation can begin, and this always proceeds by the – admittedly loose – application of the rules of implicit definition. The data are *words;* the meaning of a word in a statement is determined by comparison with other statements containing words similar to the word in question, first in the same document, then in other writings by the same author, and finally in those of other writers of the same period. In this way (as was stressed in the account of definition) the meaning of a word can be more and more closely fixed, and various hypotheses about its meaning deductively eliminated. In practice this purely semiotic proceeding is further combined with reduction, by working over a mass of historical statements, hypotheses, theories etc.: all this in order to clarify the meaning of the sign.

But with all this the historical *facts* have not yet been arrived at. Statements cannot be considered to express facts except in so far as they have acquired, somehow or other, at least one possible meaning. Only when the meaning of the words is clearly understood as the author of the text intended can an inquiry into the *truth* of the statements be begun.

Historical Criticism

After the document has been interpreted, i.e. after the historian has established what the writer intended to say, the next task is so-called historical criticism. This consists essentially in an attempt to ascertain whether the statement in question is true. The process by means of which this is done is quite clearly a process of explanation, exactly, from the logical point of view, like the one used in the natural sciences; the problem, that is to say, is solved by incorporating the statement under examination into an axiomatic system. Admittedly the axiomatic systems developed in this and other connections by historians are usually very loosely constructed, but the movement of thought does not differ from that found in the exact systems.

The system in question usually contains two classes of statements. (1) First there are certain metalinguistic or, more precisely, pragmatic statements about the author: they establish whether he was in a position to know the true state of affairs, whether he was able to report it correctly and whether he wished to do so. In this connection various special postulates are used: it is usually assumed, for example, that a man says what he really means as long as he has no particular reason to lie.

(2) Second, in the development of the system, there are statements in the object language which are obtained directly from the interpretation of documents, and also statements whose place in the discipline of history has previously been established by reductive methods. If all statements of this kind can be reconciled without contradiction with the one under examination this is an argument in favor of its truth. And the process of verification continues as further statements are derived from it in the framework of the system.

Historical Explanation

Only now can the historian proceed to genuine explanation: the whole of the work described so far served only to procure statements corresponding to the protocol statements of the natural sciences. What remains does not involve anything of fundamental importance: the attempt is made here, just as in the natural sciences, to explain these factual statements reductively, using regressive reduction as well as verification. The following are the most important differences between the application of these methods and what goes on in the natural sciences:

(1) As has already been said, induction is not used in history, that is, explanation is not carried out by means of generalizations. It does not follow from this that no general statements occur in the explanations, in fact such statements, drawn from various sciences, are regularly made use of. But in this case the statements established on the basis of reduction – which therefore correspond to the laws and theories of the natural sciences – are singular. (2) Experimentation cannot be resorted to, since the phenomena in question are individual and past. Consequently any application of Mill's or similar methods is precluded. In this probably lies one of the most important reasons for the relatively undeveloped state of history as a science. (3) Finally historical explanation is almost always genetic. This method is not restricted to the historical disciplines, but it plays a more important part in them than elsewhere. What is involved is an explanation of how an event came about, in such a way that the statement to be explained, say A, is first explained by a statement referring to the immediate past, e.g. B; then B is explained by a third statement C, which again refers to the immediate past with respect to B, etc. A genetic explanation of the outbreak of the French Revolution, for example, will not be satisfied with deducing the relevant statement, in the framework of

the system, from some statement about immediately preceding economic, social and religious conditions, but will explain these in their turn by a statement about the influence of the Encyclopedists, etc.

Historiography also constructs systems and therefore has its theories. But these theories are never general. With this reservation, the end product of historical work looks just like that of scientific work: the mass of historical statements is ordered and incorporated logically in a system. It should be obvious without further discussion that its method is typically reductive.

Final Remarks

It follows from these sketchy considerations that there certainly is such a thing as historical method, but only in a sense almost as loose as that in which we can speak of psychological, astronomical or demographic method; that is, it is a special method of the kind which every science must construct for itself. The historical method cannot by any stretch of the imagination be regarded as one of the most general methods of thought. In itself it consists of a special application of the important general methods, chiefly the reductive method. The decisive difference between what we find in history and what we find in the natural sciences lies not so much in the domain of method as of material: this is immeasurably more complicated in history and requires very complex analysis.

We do not really know what the logical structure of historical method is in detail. The impossibility of including this method among deductive and inductive methods, which were once the only methods known, seems to be the reason why most methodologists of the historical disciplines have limited themselves either to describing techniques of research, or to searching for irrational solutions to the theoretical problems of their methodology. Although the impact of the subjective is obviously very strong here, there is no need to resort to such heroic measures. The general methodology of contemporary thought provides concepts with which the historical method also can be investigated.

This investigation, in detail, is the task of the special methodology. Only a few fundamental elements of historical method have been touched on here. They have been chosen because they offer an excellent example of the fertility of the new concepts, and also because the historical method – although it is a special one – concerns a very large class of disciplines and may therefore be of greater interest than most other special methodologies.

EPILOGUE

The recent views briefly reported in this book, and the various suggested solutions of philosophical problems, lend themselves to a few reflections of a general nature. We shall divide them into two classes, those in the first referring to methodology itself but those in the second expressing philosophical opinions about human thought and knowledge.

In regard to methodology itself three things should be said:

– that it is developing today both rapidly and successfully. It is perhaps not exaggerating to assert that it has rarely been as eagerly worked at as in our time.

– that this development has brought with it a number of new insights and the development of earlier insights. As evidence of this it is enough to point to the working out of the phenomenological method, the insight into the importance of linguistic analysis, the new classification of processes of thought and the development of the axiomatic system.

– that in spite of this – or perhaps because of it – contemporary methodology is struggling with many unsolved problems. Among these are the old problem of induction, the quite new problem of the meaning of hypotheses and the possibility of ascertaining their probability, and the not yet fully clarified problem of the relativity of systems of logic.

With respect to philosophical questions in general one might perhaps venture the following assertions on the basis of recent views:

– that the expressions "thought", "knowledge", "the acquisition of knowledge", and therefore also "science" and "truth" and other similar expressions, are not straightforward but highly ambiguous (in an analogical sense, to use a scholastic expression). Contemporary methodology shows how diverse are the methods, and the value of their results, in various disciplines.

– that every simple solution of the problem of knowledge must be rejected as inadequate. Reality, and hence the thought which tries to take it in, are obviously of enormous complexity. Any attempt to make this work simple – narrow dogmatism no less than idle relativism and scepticism – springs from a complete misunderstanding.

126

– that scientists and philosophers – in spite of what they often say themselves – cling to a fundamental belief in the value of rational thought: for methodology is nothing but an account of the variety of methods which have been developed – especially in recent years – in order to make rational thinking possible.

Some conclusions follow from all this as to the present situation of philosophy. It is unfortunately marked by a sharp division. At international congresses there is often no longer any dialogue but rather an exchange of monologues: the proponents of phenomenology and of linguistic analysis confront one another with a complete lack of mutual understanding. But in the light of what present-day methodology has to say to us the various methods of thought are not mutually exclusive alternatives, but complementary aspects of thought. An adequate contemporary philosophy should not reject any method, especially since it can be known from methodology how difficult it is to arrive at valid results.

It follows further that it might perhaps be possible to speak of an authentic philosophical method, if only philosophers would not commit themselves *a priori* to one of the many available methods, but would instead, following the tradition of the great thinkers, consider *nihil humani a se alienum*. This philosophical method would rest on a phenomenological analysis. But it would not stop there, on the one hand applying analysis to what exists and to its existence, on the other hand – conscious of human fallibility – using linguistic analysis widely and finally appealing to the results of the reductive sciences.

Such a philosophy is urgently needed today, at a time when knowledge has become so specialized. It is the more necessary in that mankind – more now perhaps than in other epochs – is abandoning itself only too often to blind and uncontrolled instincts. Knowledge and reason are threatened today as rarely before, and with them everything human, perhaps human existence itself. Only a genuine philosophy bringing *all* available resources to bear on the search for knowledge could provide a remedy for this situation; it will not come from particular sciences or from other comparatively simple systems which, committed to a single method, are incapable of taking in the whole.

GUIDE TO FURTHER READING*

I. INTRODUCTION

Pfänder, Maritain, Carnap (6).

II. THE PHENOMENOLOGICAL METHOD

Basic work: HUSSERL (1).
Best account: HEIDEGGER pp. 49ff. See also FARBER, TYMIENIECKA.
Examples of application: HUSSERL (1) (2), SCHELER (1) (2), INGARDEN (1) (2).

By contrast most *treatises* under the title of 'Phenomenology' do not deal with methodology as it is understood in this book; they are useful for an understanding of other philosophical aspects of phenomenology: VAN BREDA, MERLEAU-PONTY, REINACH.

III. SEMIOTIC METHODS

Bibliography: CHURCH, BETH (1).
Current bibliography: 'The Journal of Symbolic Logic' 1936ff.
Basic works: CARNAP (1), TARSKI (1), MORRIS (1) (2).
Developed system: CARNAP (3) (4).
Problem of verification: CARNAP (2), REICHENBACH (1), HEMPEL (1).
Periodicals: 'The Journal of Symbolic Logic', 'Philosophy of Science', 'The British Journal for the Philosophy of Science', 'Mind'.

IV. THE AXIOMATIC METHOD

Bibliography: CHURCH, BETH (1).
Current bibliography: 'The Journal of Symbolic Logic' 1936ff.
Basic works in mathematical logic: WHITEHEAD-RUSSELL, HILBERT (2).
Principal textbooks: BETH (2), DOPP, PRIOR, QUINE (1) (2).
Short Treatments: BOCHEŃSKI, BECKER, CARNAP (6), HILBERT (1), TARSKI (3).
Technique of axiomatic systems: WEYL, WOODGER (for Tarski's system).
On definition: DUBISLAV, ROBINSON.
Periodicals: 'The Journal of Symbolic Logic', 'Philosophy of Science', 'The British Journal for the Philosophy of Science', 'Mind'.

V. REDUCTIVE METHODS

Recent comprehensive works: BRAITHWAITE, KNEALE, NAGEL (2), POPPER, REICHEN-

---

* *Translator's note:* In this list and in the bibliography (p. 130) I have retained all Bocheński's references, giving versions in English where they are available, and have also added one or two titles which have appeared since the publication of the original.

BACH (1), SCHLESINGER, WEYL, VON WRIGHT (1) (2); *among earlier works:* BROAD, NICOD.

Collections of important papers: FEIGL-BRODBECK, WIENER.

Historical works: DUHEM (earlier), THORNDIKE (basic).

Concept formation: HEMPEL (2).

Probability: CARNAP (5), KEYNES, VON MISES, NAGEL (1) (synopsis of problems).

History: MEYERHOFF, WAGNER (with full bibliography; includes an account of irrationalist interpretations of method, due in essentials to Dilthey, which is useful for an understanding of philosophical and other special problems in this field).

Detailed bibliography and account of the methodological opinions of scientists: BAVINK.

BIBLIOGRAPHY*

BAVINK, B.: *The Anatomy of Modern Science*, 1932 (1914).

BECKER, O.: *Einführung in die logistik*, 1951.

BERGSON, H.:
  (1) *Time and Free Will, an Essay on the Immediate Data of Consciousness*, 1910 (1889).
  (2) *Creative Evolution*, 1911 (1907).

BETH, E. W.:
  (1) *Symbolische Logik und Grundlegung der exakten Wissenschaften*, 1948.
  (2) *The Foundations of Mathematics*, 1959 (1950).

BOCHEŃSKI, J.: *Precis of Mathematical Logic*, 1959 (1948).

BOLZANO, B.: *Wissenschaftslehre* (4 vols.) 1837.

BRAITHWAITE, R. B.: *Scientific Explanation*, 1953.

VAN BREDA, H. L. (ed.): *Problèmes actuels de la phénoménologie*, 1952.

BROAD, C. D.: *Scientific Thought*, 1923.

CARNAP, R.:
  (1) *Logical Syntax of Language*, 1937 (1934).
  (2) 'Testability and Meaning', *Phil. Sci.* 3 (1937); new ed. 1950.
  (3) *Introduction to Semantics*, 1942.
  (4) *Formalization of Logic*, 1943.
  (5) *Logical Foundations of Probability*, 1950.
  (6) *Introduction to Symbolic Logic*, 1958 (1954).

CHURCH, A.: 'A Bibliography of Symbolic Logic', *JSL* 1 (1936) and later additions in the same journal.

DOPP, J.: *Formal Logic*, 1960 (1949–50).

DUBISLAV, W.: *Die Definition*, 1931.

---

* Here only the titles of works referred to in the text and in the 'Guide to Further Reading' are given. (*Translator's note:* for works translated into English the date in parentheses is that of publication in the original language.)

DUHEM, P.:
  (1) *Le Système du Monde* (5 vols.) 1913ff.
  (2) *The Aim and Structure of Physical Theory*, 1954 (1906).
FARBER, M.: *Foundations of Phenomenology*, 1943.
FEIGL, H. and BRODBECK, M.: *Readings in the Philosophy of Science*, 1953.
FREGE, G.: 'On Sense and Reference' (1892), in *Translations from the Philosophical Writings of Gottlob Frege*, 1952.
HARTMANN, N.:
  (1) *Zur Grundlegung der Ontologie*, 1935.
  (2) *New Ways of Ontology*, 1953 (1948)
HEIDEGGER, M.: *Being and Time*, 1962 (1927).
HEMPEL, C. G.:
  (1) 'Problems and changes in the empiricist criterion of meaning', *Rev. Int. de Philos.* 2 (1950).
  (2) *Fundamentals of Concept Formation in Empirical Science*, 1952.
HEYTING, A.:
  (1) *Die formalen Regeln der intuitionischen Logik*, 1930.
  (2) *Mathematische grundlagenforschung: intuitionismus, beweistheorie*, 1934.
  (3) *Intuitionism – An Introduction*, 1956.
HILBERT, D.:
  (1) and ACKERMANN, W.: *Principles of Mathematical Logic*, 1950 (1928).
  (2) and BERNAYS, P.: *Grundlagen der Mathematik* (2 vols), 1934–9.
HUSSERL, E.:
  (1) *Logische Untersuchungen* (2 vols.)1901ff.
  (2) *Ideas*, 1931 (1913).
INGARDEN, R.:
  (1) *Essentiale Fragen*, 1924.
  (2) *Das literarische Kunstwerk*, 1931.
JASPERS, K.:
  (1) *Philosophie*, 1932.
  (2) *Von der Wahrheit*, 1947.
ŁUKASIEWICZ, J.:
  (1) O logice trójwartościowej (On three-valued logic), *Ruch filozoficzny* 5 (1920).
  (2) *'Philosophische Bemerkungen zu mehrwertigen Systemen des Aussagenkalkuls'*, *Comptes rend. Soc. Sci. et lettres de Varsovie*, Cl III, 1930.
  (3) *W sprawie odwracalnosci stosunku racji i nastepstwa* (On the inconvertibility of the relation of ground and consequent) *Przegl. fil.* 16 (1913).
MARCEL, G.: *Le Monde Cassée*, 1933.
MARITAIN, G.: *Introduction to Logic*, 1937.
MERLEAU-PONTY, M.: *Phenomenology of Perception*, 1962 (1945).
MEYERHOFF, H. (ed.): *The Philosophy of History in Our Time*, 1959.
MILL, John Stuart: *A System of Logic* (2 vols.), 1843.
MISES, R. von: *Probability, Statistics, and Truth*, 1939 (1928).
MORRIS, Charles:
  (1) *Foundations of the theory of signs*, 1938.
  (2) *Signs, language, and behavior*, 1946.
NAGEL, E.:
  (1) *Principles of the Theory of Probability*, 1939.
  (2) *The Structure of Science*, 1961.

NICOD, J.: *Foundations of Geometry and Induction*, 1930 (1923).

OGDEN, C. K. and RICHARDS, I. A.: *The Meaning of Meaning*, 1949.

PFÄNDER, A.: *Logik*, 1929.

POPPER, K.: *The Logic of Discovery*, 1959 (1935).

POST, E.: *Introduction to a general theory of elementary propositions*, Am. J. Math. 43 (1921).

PRIOR, A. N.: *Formal Logic*, 1955.

QUINE, W. V.:
(1) *Mathematical Logic*, 1940.
(2) *Methods of Logic*, 1950.

REICHENBACH, H.:
(1) *Experience and Prediction*, 1938.
(2) *Philosophic Foundations of Quantum Mechanics*, 1944.

REINACH, A.: *Was ist Phänomenologie?* 1951.

SCHELER, M.:
(1) *Der Formalismus in der Ethik und die materiale Wertethik*, 1913–1916.
(2) *The Nature of Sympathy*, 1954 (1913).

SCHLESINGER, G.: *Method in the Physical Sciences*, 1963.

TARSKI, A.:
(1) The Concept of Truth in Formalized Languages, (1931), and
(2) Foundations of the calculus of systems, (1935), both in *Logic, Semantics, Metamathematics*, 1956.

THORNDIKE, L.: *A History of Magic and Experimental Science* (6 vols.), 1923ff.

TYMIENIECKA, Anna-Teresa: *Phenomenology and Science in Contemporary European Thought*, 1962.

WAGNER, Tr.: *Geschichtswissenschaft*, 1951.

WEYL, H.: *Philosophy of Mathematics and Natural Science*, 1949 (1928).

WHITEHEAD, A. N. and RUSSELL, B.: *Principia Mathematica* (3 vols.), 1910–1913.

WIENER, P.: *Readings in Philosophy of Science*, 1953.

WITTGENSTEIN, L.: *Tractatus Logico-Philosophicus*, 1922 (1921).

WOODGER, J.:
(1) *The axiomatic method in biology*, 1937.
(2) *The technique of theory construction*, 1939.

VON WRIGHT, G. H.:
(1) *A treatise on induction and probability*, 1951.
(2) *The logical problem of induction*, 1957.

INDEX OF PERSONS

132

INDEX OF SUBJECTS